# A QUESTION
# OF BOXING
## 1,500 QUESTIONS ON
## THE SPORT OF BOXING

# A QUESTION OF BOXING

# 1,500 QUESTIONS ON THE SPORT OF BOXING

## RALPH OATES

COVER PHOTOGRAPH

## MUHAMMAD ALI

(COURTESY OF DEREK ROWE)

First published 2021 by DB Publishing, an imprint of JMD Media Ltd,
Nottingham, United Kingdom.

Copyright © Ralph Oates

ISBN 9781780916200

# FOREWORD

Since 2012 British amateur squads have made great strides at Commonwealth, European, World and Olympic level and some of those who have had success have gone on to great things as professionals.

Even allowing for the proliferation of 'world' titles in the professional game, some of ours who hold or have held 'world' titles have actually proved themselves number one at their weight.

In the world at large, beyond the UK, the best compare well with the greats of the past and many of those past greats we revere would surely have boxed at a division or two lower than they did. Had they been able to benefit from modern scientific nutrition and training techniques.

So boxing, both in the UK and the rest of the world, looks set for a bright future.

However, a sport as compelling as boxing can never just be about now or the future. With a history going back 400 years to the start of the bare-knuckle era, the past will always remain a treasure trove of information, always there waiting to be rediscovered by every new generation of 'aficionados'. I thought I knew quite a bit about our sport's history, at least I did until I started reading Ralph Oates's books.

Ralph is a historian 'par excellence' and his many past books have proved an education for all boxing fans

This one will be ideal for so many – those who already know a bit, those who love the game but have no idea about its history, those who just love collecting sporting facts and those who need some of those facts to compile pub quizzes; those, as well, who are just starting out in the sport, whether having joined an amateur club or just a new fan watching from ringside or on television. There are also those, like me, who were around at times in the past to which some of the questions relate but who still struggle sometimes with answers, always just on the tip of our tongues, to quiz questions we know we should know,

This book is an ideal Christmas present, New Year present, birthday present or maybe just as a 'thank you' or an 'I love you' to the boxing nut in your life.

Can't wait to try it out on some of my fellow boxing nuts!

## Simon Block

Member of the Board of Governors, World Boxing Council
Vice President, Hastings Ex-Boxers Association
Former General Secretary, British Boxing Board of Control
Former Hon Secretary, Commonwealth Boxing Council

# ABOUT THE AUTHOR

Boxing Gloves is Ralph Oates's 12th book about boxing, his previous publications being *World heavyweight Boxing Champions Elite* (1987), *Know Your Boxing* (1991), *Boxing Clever* (1994), *Boxing Shadows* (1997), *The Heavyweight Boxing Quiz Book* (2002), *Muhammad Ali Boxing Quiz Book* (2007), *The Ultimate Boxing Quiz Book* (2009), *The World Champions Boxing Quiz Book* (2013), *The Noble Art of Heavyweight Boxing* (2015), *Bruno and Lewis: The Boxing Years* (2017) and *A Round of Boxing: A Trip Through Time* (2019).

Ralph, a former amateur boxer, also wrote articles for The British Boxing Board of Control Yearbook for 18 years – a publication which was the leading book of its kind. He had his own regular weekly boxing column in the *Essex Courier* and one in *Take One* – a monthly paper – and *Bounce* – a monthly magazine. He is also a former boxing consultant for the Guinness World Records. The national TV quiz show *Who Dares Wins* also used questions by Ralph on two occasions.

**Ralph will be donating the royalties from the book to The Ringside Charitable Trust.**

# ACKNOWLEDGEMENTS

It of course takes a great deal of research to put a quiz book together – every question needs to be checked and every answer also needs to be verified. So my personal thanks must go to my brother, Howard Oates, for his keen assistance in helping to check the said information in this publication – needless to say it was no easy task. Howard has also written books not on boxing but on the sport of Judo, whereupon he is a former British champion and now a top trainer in the sport, producing a number of top competitors.

Another thank you must go to my very good friend Simon Block for taking the time to pen the foreword for the book. The photographs that appear in the book are courtesy of Derek Rowe, Philip Sharkey and Les Clark. Sadly, Les passed away in 2015; however, his wife Jackie Clark kindly gave me her permission to use the images. All three photographers are obviously well respected within their trade for their excellent work. Thanks also go to Denise Oates for her technical assistance. I must also thank the team at JMD Media – Michelle Grainger, Matt Limbert and of course Steve Caron, who have all worked hard in helping to produce the book.

I also dedicate the book to the memory of Ruby Oates, who was a very special lady.

# CONTENTS

# WEIGHT DIVISIONS
# IN THE PROFESSIONAL RANKS

**(The following weight divisions are referred to in this book)**

| | |
|---|---|
| Minimumweight/Strawweight | 105 lbs/7st 7lbs |
| Light-flyweight | 108lbs/7st 10lbs |
| Flyweight | 112lbs/8st |
| Super-flyweight | 115 lbs/8st 3lbs |
| Bantamweight | 118 lbs/8st 6lbs |
| Super-bantamweight | 122lbs/8st 10lbs |
| Featherweight | 126lbs/9st |
| Super-featherweight | 130lbs/9st 4lbs |
| Lightweight | 135lbs/9st 9lbs |
| Super-lightweight | 140lbs/10st |
| Welterweight | 147 lbs/10st 7lbs |
| Super-welterweight | 154lbs/11st |
| Middleweight | 160 lbs/11st 6lbs |
| Super-middleweight | 168lbs/12st |
| Light-heavyweight | 175 lbs/12st 7lbs |
| Cruiserweight | 200 lbs/14st 4lbs |
| Heavyweight | Over 200 lbs/14st 4lbs |

# WORLD BOXING ORGANISATIONS

**(The following boxing organisations are referenced to in the book)**

| | |
|---|---|
| **WBC** | World Boxing Council |
| **WBA** | World Boxing Association |
| **WBO** | World Boxing Organisation |
| **WBU** | World Boxing Union |
| **WBF** | World Boxing Foundation |
| **WIBF** | Women's International Boxing Federation |
| **IBF** | International Boxing Federation |
| **IBA** | International Boxing Association |
| **IBO** | International Boxing Organisation |
| **NY** | New York |
| **NBA** | National Boxing Association |
| **EBU** | European Boxing Union |

**Please note** The Commonwealth Championship in bygone years was known as the Empire title. However, I have used the term Commonwealth throughout the book for simplicity.

# INTRODUCTION

I have been intrigued by boxing for many years, even participating as a boxer for a time in the amateurs, sadly having to call it a day when becoming short-sighted. When this happened, it was a very hard blow to say the very least, one much harder than I had ever endured when boxing. It was a situation I couldn't change. To quote the often-used expression, it is what it is, or since it happened in the past perhaps I should say it was what it was. Worse things happen in life and this was just a setback along the way.  To use boxing terminology, you have to role with the punches and take it on the chin once in a while, and if you're put on the canvas you have to get up and fight on like a champion. While I did fairly well when boxing, I knew deep down that I was not going to be a champion of any description. I was not going to be a sensation that had people talking and watching in amazement. So, in all truth, I was no great loss to the world of boxing. Nevertheless, it really is difficult to walk away from a sport that you enjoy. This is something many fighters feel once their boxing days come to an end, especially those who had been champions during their careers. Sadly, many boxers fight on even when it is clear their best days are well behind them and will not return anytime soon. The result being they will often lose to opponents whom they would have defeated easily in their prime. It is often sad to see a man who once held the status of world champion become a stepping stone for up and coming fighters who need a big name to pad their record.  Many members of the public cannot understand why these fighters ignore the obvious signs that it's over and they should be sensible and walk away from the sweet science. Why do they continue in a sport that is so difficult, so demanding and often so painful? To fully understand that you would need to be a fighter and understand a fighter's mindset. Their desire to do battle inside a ring, often walking through adversity to gain the win or at least put on a good show, rarely goes away, it is routed in their soul, it is part of their very being. To advise a boxer that he should not fight again is something he doesn't want to hear – his reaction is akin to a bird with a broken wing realising that he will not be able to take to the air and fly again. There are many boxers, of course, who do take heed of the deterioration in their work and quit at the right time. They are able to maintain their interest in the sport by becoming trainers, promoters, referees, judges and managers etc, giving back to the sport which they had served so well over the years. This also gives them a renewed interest, a focal point to concentrate on and the contentment of still being around the fight game in some capacity. Yet there is no doubt they miss the training, the roar of the crowd, and the feeling of anticipation before a forthcoming contest. It isn't just a sport, it's a way of life, which is difficult to give up. While a number of fighters face reality and accept that their boxing days are over, some sadly, after a period of retirement, decide to put the gloves back on and step between the ropes once again, making an ill-advised comeback to the square ring which often ends in defeat. Hence the old adage they never comeback, a fact which has proven to be correct more often than not. A few fighters have been able to return with a moderate degree of success against lower-level opponents, but they are never able to recapture the golden years of their youth, the clock cannot be turned back. Old Father Time is an opponent who cannot be beaten, delayed a little, maybe, but never beaten – he is relentless. When the returning fighter eventually steps up a level against an ambitious youngster, he often finds to his dismay that the well has run dry – he has nothing left to give – suffering a heavy defeat in the process, which finally convinces him that his fighting days are well and truly over and he has heard the bell sound for the final time. A sad exit but one which is seen all too often in the sport.

Like so many, I found myself still strongly attracted to boxing after I said goodbye to the sport. I may not have been able to throw punches in combat any longer, but this did not dampen my interest in boxing. I continued to follow the game with keen enthusiasm, taking careful note of the results from all over the world, observing the emerging fighters who would one day develop into champions, those who had that special something and would duly go on to become not just world title holders but legends, and thus add to the rich pages of boxing history. I eventually decided to turn my hand to writing and put together a number of books over the years, which have contained many facts about the fighters who have laced on the gloves and the contests they took part in.

Many boxers who have graced the ring over the years have become so popular that even members of the public who do not normally take an interest in the sport know their names and have been thrilled by their exploits in the ring. While each weight division has produced outstanding fighters, there is no argument that it is the heavyweight poundage that captures the media's attention. The big boys are the fighters who draw the crowds. Any new prospect at heavyweight who shows any kind of potential will be under public scrutiny from the off. By comparison, a boxer from another weight category with equal or perhaps even more skill will attract less attention from the media. The world heavyweight championship is the ultimate prize, the most sought-after title in boxing. Every country wants a fighter who will become king of the poundage. It is the banner division. For many years, the USA dominated the division, producing champion after champion, they appeared unbeatable, giants among giants who were so superior in every department and would be regarded as greats in the years that followed. The odd lapse occurred now and then when a fighter from another nation had the temerity to upset the odds and take the title from the defending champion. This was big news that often shook the boxing world to its core and seemed unbelievable. The non-American who dared to take the crown found that his reign did not last too long. The championship was soon returned to the land of the stars and stripes when another American was able to take the title back. The division, it seems, was the property of the USA and they held the championship with a grip of iron. However, situations change and in recent times there's been a shift in power, it's apparent that the American hold over the heavyweight division has been well and truly broken.  No longer is it a given that when an American steps into the ring to fight for the heavyweight title, he will emerge victorious. A number of fighters outside of the USA have stepped up and shown that they have the talent and are now equal to the task and have become world champions at the weight.

Boxing is a sport that has clearly produced many facts of interest, a number of which have left a lasting memory in the minds of those who follow the sport. After meeting many fight fans over the years, I have observed just how much they like to talk about their favourite sport whenever the opportunity arises. They keenly exchange points of view doing their conversation, sharing information about the nights when they witnessed exciting fights. The magical moment when they saw at first hand boxing history being made inside the square ring, the night when the underdog surprised and went against all predictions by defeating the firm favourite –when the impossible became possible. When the dream of the contender became a reality by him winning the world title.  The excitement when a losing fighter turned the tide with one punch to claim victory, surprising both his opponent and fans. One, however, has to question the validity of those memories with the passing of time. Can we still be positive that A stopped B in round seven or was it round eight? Did C fight in the southpaw stance or was he orthodox? These are just a couple of examples that often test us when thinking back on our sport. It can often be difficult to remember who did what and when, even by the most prolific followers of boxing, but then that is what makes this book a challenge.

There have been many changes within the sport over the years. There was a time when professional boxing had just eight weight divisions, but that number has grown substantiality and at the moment there are now 17, with each of the four major boxing organisations complicating matters by often recognising different title holders at the same poundage. If that wasn't enough, it was announced in 2020 that a new weight division, the Bridgerweight, would be introduced by the WBC in 2021. This, of course, will bring the total of divisions up to 18. This division would sit between the cruiserweight and heavyweight division. No doubt the other organisations will eventually follow suit, giving the sport even more champions, each holding a version of the title. To add to the confusion, let's not forget that there are also super, regular, interim, silver, gold and franchise champions in the mix. We now have a situation whereby even the keenest fan is often unable to name the various fighters and who the actual champions are these days and that is not good.

So the question often comes up who really is the best in at any particular poundage? Who is the real-world champion? Now and again the various champions do meet in unifications bouts to find the undisputed title holder at the respective weight. However, such occasions are rare and when a fighter is able to obtain such status he will find it difficult to hold on to the four championship belts. This is because he will find it impossible to carry out the demands of the rival organisations, who will want him to meet their mandatory challenger within a stipulated time period. Often the respected boxer will either be stripped of the title or will relinquish the belt to the governing body whom he cannot appease. The two top-ranked fighters will then step up to fight for the vacant crown with the winner becoming the new champion. (Depending on the organisation involved the interim or regular champion is often made full champion) Then we are back to square one, with the title once again being fragmented. To a certain extent, the boxer who wins the vacant title while the stripped champion is still active is not, in reality, taken too seriously as a world-title holder by the fans. He may have gained world-title status, but to many he will be regarded as wearing a cardboard crown until he finally crosses gloves with the real champion.

Many traditionalists feel it would be far better for the sport if there was just one world boxing organisation with one champion in each weight division. Thus, the world title holders would be easier to identity and the confusion of who is the real king in the said weight division would be clarified once and for all. Looking at the situation logically, this would seem to be the ideal way to run the sport. One champion in each weight division makes good sense. However, we all know that good sense and logic are words which are often ignored. It must be said the one world boxing organisation scenario is not likely to happen any time soon, if at all. So this is something we must all get used to, like it or not. Looking at the other side of the argument, there is a plus factor that with there being more champions many fighters are now getting an opportunity to challenge for a world crown. There was a time in the past when good, indeed exceptional, fighters who were more than deserving of a title shot failed to get their chance or were past their best when the opportunity finally came their way. The then-reigning world title holders defended their crown on average three times a year and hence were unable to accommodate all of the various contenders who were knocking at the championship door eager to get their shot.

We sometimes hear older followers of boxing stating that the ring men of yesteryear were far superior to the ones we see in action today. They were more talented, tougher, fitter and stronger. They would most certainly put today's ring gladiators in their place. Is that true? It is a theme which constantly resurfaces when comparing boxers from different time periods. For example, at heavyweight would Muhammad Ali have had the skills to defeat Joe Louis or would Louis have found a way to overcome him by finding a chink in his armour. Staying with the heavyweights division, would the hard-hitting Rocky Marciano have been able to beat the equally hard-hitting Mike Tyson had they shared the ring together when both at the top of their game and in their prime? That bout would have been an exciting slugfest for sure. How would middleweight Sugar Ray Robinson have coped with Marvin Hagler when both were at their very best? Staying with Robinson when boxing at welterweight, would he have been able to out box Sugar Ray Leonard? Great fighters in many other weight divisions are also compared. Truthfully, it is a debate that is interesting but is really pointless. Each fighter from another time should be respected and appreciated for the era they fought in. Statistics can be presented to back up the theory on who was best and who would have won had they crossed gloves, but it is just that, a theory, one which cannot be proven. The only way to settle the argue is for the fighters to meet in the ring and that, of course, is impossible due to the time period between their careers. What we should do is accept that there have been a number of fighters who have been great through the years and embrace that fact. We are very fortunate that the sport still continues to produce outstanding boxers who will, in the future, earn the accolade of being regarded as a great and hence earn their right to stand with the past greats who have fought in the ring. It should also not be forgotten that boxing has also caught the eye of a number of film producers over the years, many of whom have thus brought some fantastic movies to the big screen based on the sport – some fiction some factual. Also, a number of fighters have shown their acting ability by appearing in an assortment of roles in both film, television and on the stage.

It does not end there: some have even gone as far as venturing into the recording studios to cut a disc.

We now see that female boxing is gaining momentum and is capturing the imagination of the fans. It's not been an easy ride for them. The ladies have had to battle long and hard to get accepted and hence taken seriously, and there were times when it seemed their efforts would be futile, but to their credit they have shown their fighting spirit and fought on despite the general perception that a boxing ring was no place for a lady. In recent years, their perseverance has been duly rewarded and many are now fighting in major arenas around the world. A number of lady fighters are showing, from their exploits inside the ring, that their boxing skills should be respected and potential greats look likely to emerge from their ranks in the fullness of time. It should not be forgotten that women have also played other roles in boxing, such as managers, referees, promoters, trainers, master of ceremonies and judges. So no one can say they haven't paid their dues in the sport.

Now, there are many outstanding fighters in each weight division, showing their class, and who will eventually be involved in big promotions which will generate interest and hopefully bring new fans into the fold.

The book endeavours to test your knowledge on both the past to the present in all weight divisions, including both men and women, to see just how much you know about boxing – are you a champion or a contender, can you punch your weight when it comes to answering questions about the sport? You will soon find out. Some of the questions are easy while others are difficult. The great fighters like Muhammad Ali, Joe Louis, Rocky Marciano and Sugar Ray Robinson are included in the book, how could they not be? The new breed of fighters like Tyson Fury, Anthony Joshua, Gennady Golovkin, Deontay Wilder and Vasiliy Lomachenko are also found within the pages of the book. The questions are presented in multiple choice so this will give you a fighting chance of finding the right answers to the questions posed. I hope that you will enjoy and have fun with the book. Now go to your corners put your thinking caps on and come out fighting.

## Ralph Oates

# PROFESSIONAL DEBUTS

*In which year did the following boxers make their professional debut?*

**1. Muhammad Ali**
(a) 1960 (a) 1961 (c) 1962

**2. Frank Bruno**
(a) 1981 (b) 1982 (c) 1983

**3. Ken Buchanan**
(a) 1963 (b) 1964 (c) 1965

**4. Donald Curry**
(a) 1978 (b) 1980 (c) 1981

**5. Roberto Duran**
(a) 1968 (b) 1969 (c) 1970

**6. Bob Foster**
(a) 1959 (b) 1960 (c) 1961

**7. Emile Griffith**
(a) 1956 (b) 1958 (c) 1959

**8. Marvin Hagler**
(a) 1971 (b) 1972 (c) 1973

**9. Ismael Laguna**
(a) 1958 (b) 1960 (c) 1961

**10. Floyd Patterson**
(a) 1952 (b) 1953 (c) 1954

**11. Roy Jones Jr.**
(a) 1987 (b) 1988 (c) 1989

**12. Sugar Ray Leonard**
(a) 1975 (b) 1976 (c) 1977

**13. Lennox Lewis**
(a) 1989 (b) 1990 (c) 1991

**14. Alan Minter**
(a) 1970 (b) 1971 (c) 1972

**15. Carlos Monzon**

(a) 1963 (b) 1964 (c) 1965

**16. John H. Stracey**

(a) 1969 (b) 1970 (c) 1971

**17. Ernie Terrell**

(a) 1955 (b) 1956 (c) 1957

**18. Rodrigo Valdez**

(a) 1962 (b) 1963 (c) 1964

**19. Jim Watt**

(a) 1968 (b) 1969 (c) 1970

**20. Howard Winstone**

(a) 1958 (b) 1959 (c) 1960

# FIRST PROFESSIONAL OPPONENTS

*Who was the first professional opponent of the following boxers?*

**1. Virgil Akins**
(a) Albert Adams (b) Charlie Baxter (c) Ollie Cobbins

**2. Terry Allen**
(a) Douglas Claxton (b) Ron Kingston (c) Jim Thomas

**3. Jose Becerra**
(a) Miguel Estrada (b) Ray Gomez (c) Lorenzo Ibarra

**4. Jimmy Carruthers**
(a) Ted Fitzgerald (b) Ron Wilson (c) Fred Kay

**5. Gene Fullmer**
(a) Andy Jackson (b) Gary Carr (c) Glen Peck

**6. Rocky Graziano**
(a) Mike Mastandrea (b) Curtis Hightower (c) Kenny Blackmar

**7. Ricky Hatton**
(a) Colin McAuley (b) Robert Alvarez (c) David Thompson

**8. Larry Holmes**
(a) Curtis Whitener (b) Art Savage (c) Rodell Dupree

**9. Danny Lopez**
(a) Filiberto Castro (b) Steve Flajole (c) Mauro Olivares

**10. Terry Marsh**
(a) Dave Sullivan (b) Ian Kid Murray (c) Andrew DaCosta

**11. Michael Nunn**
(a) Ismael Templos (b) John Borman (c) Robert Waymon Jackson

**12. Willie Pastrano**
(a) Domingo Rivera (b) Frankie Speed (c) Jimmy Conino

**13. Raul Rojas**
(a) Frankie Corpus (b) Ray Coleman (c) Freddie Burris

**14. Barney Ross**
(a) Joe Borola (b) Virgil Tobin (c) Ramon Lugo

**15. John H. Stracey**

(a) Ronnie Clifford (b) Santos Martins (c) Ray Opuku

**16. Johnny Tapia**

(a) Efren Chavez (b) James Dean (c) Norberto Ayala

**17. James Toney**

(a) Ronnie Yoe (b) Stephen Lee (c) Carl Penn

**18. Paul Weir**

(a) Eddie Vallejo (b) Louis Veitch (c) Neil Parry

**19. Ike Williams**

(a) Leroy Born (b) Patsy Gall (c) Carmine Fotti

**20. Howard Winstone**

(a) Peter Sexton (b) Billy Graydon (c) Tommy Williams

# LAST PROFESSIONAL OPPONENTS

***Who was the last professional opponent of the following boxers?***

**1. Henry Armstrong**
(a) Genaro Rojo (b) Chester Slider (c) Mike Belloise

**2. Jack Britton**
(a) Rudy Marshall (b) Bobby Ruffalo (c) Alf Schell

**3. Chucho Castillo**
(a) Danny Lopez (b) Rafael Ortega (c) Ernesto Herrera

**4. Donald Curry**
(a) Gary Jones (b) Emmett Linton (c) Terry Norris

**5. Flash Elorde**
(a) Hiroyuki Murakami (b) Shunkichi Suemitsu (c) Isao Ichihara

**6. Fighting Harada**
(a) Pat Gonzales (b) Johnny Famechon (c) Vil Tumulak

**7. Matthew Hilton**
(a) Darrell Flint (b) Kevin Daigle (c) Clarence White

**8. Bernard Hopkins**
(a) Sergey Kovalev (b) Beibut Shumenov (c) Joe Smith Jr

**9. Marvin Johnson**
(a) Jean Marie Emebe (b) Leslie Stewart (c) Frank Lux

**10. Ricardo Lopez**
(a) Zolani Petelo (b) Anucha Phothong (c) Will Grigsby

**11. Charlie Magri**
(a) Sot Chitalada (b) Franco Cherchi (c) Duke Mckenzie

**12. Alan Minter**
(a) Tony Sibson (b) Mustafa Hamsho (c) Ernie Singletary

**13. Carlos Monzon**
(a) Gratien Tonna (b) Tony Licata (c) Rodrigo Valdez

**14. Jose Napoles**
(a) Armando Muniz (b) John H. Stracey (c) Horacio Agustin Saldano

### 15. Ken Norton
(a) Randall Cobb (b) Gerry Cooney (c) Scott LeDoux

### 16. Jackie Paterson
(a) Willie Myles (b) Eddie Carson (c) Vic Toweel

### 17. Mando Ramos
(a) Antonio Leyva (b) Al Franklin (c) Wayne Beale

### 18. Sandy Saddler
(a) Larry Boardman (b) George Monroe (c) Flash Elorde

### 19. Vic Toweel
(a) Carmelo Costa (b) Harry Walker (c) Ronnie Clayton

### 20. Pernell Whitaker
(a) Carlos Bojorquez (b) Felix Trinidad (c) Andrey Pestryaev

ROUND FOUR

# OPPONENTS NOT MET
# IN A PROFESSIONAL CAREER

*Which opponent did the following boxers __not__ meet during their professional careers?*

*1. Muhammad Ali*
(a) Juergen Blin (b) Thad Spencer (c) Mac Foster

*2. Henry Armstrong*
(a) Jake LaMotta (b) Sugar Ray Robinson (c) Beau Jack

*3. Frank Bruno*
(a) Gerrie Coetzee (b) Joe Bugner (c) Pinklon Thomas

*4. Joe Calzaghe*
(a) Carl Froch (b) Charles Brewer (c) Byron Mitchell

*5. Donald Curry*
(a) Bruce Finch (b) Kirkland Laing (c) Marlon Starling

*6. Bob Foster*
(a) Victor Galindez (b) Zora Folley (c) Ernie Terrell

*7. Joe Frazier*
(a) Eddie Machen (b) Doug Jones (c) Earnie Shavers

*8. Thomas Hearns*
(a) Tony Sibson (b) Angel Espada (c) Murray Sutherland

*9. Rafael Herrera*
(a) Lupe Gonzalez (b) Chucho Castillo (c) Alan Rudkin

*10. Larry Holmes*
(a) Greg Page (b) Fred Askew (c) Earnie Shavers

*11. Lloyd Honeyghan*
(a) Roger Stafford (b) Jun-Suk Hwang (c) Sylvester Mittee

*12. Julian Jackson*
(a) Rafael Corona (b) Mike McCallum (c) Fred Hutchings

*13. Lennox Lewis*
(a) Ossie Ocasio (b) Tim Witherspoon (c) Mike Weaver

### 14. Walter McGowan

(a) Jose Medel (b) John McCluskey (c) Ray Perez

### 15. Colin McMillan

(a) Gary De'Roux (b) Sean Murphy (c) Paul Hodkinson

### 16. Rocky Marciano

(a) Nino Valdes (b) Johnny Pretzie (c) Pete Louthis

### 17. Carlos Palomino

(a) Hedgemon Lewis (b) Roberto Duran (c) Cuby Jackson

### 18. Vicente Saldivar

(a) Dwight Hawkins (b) Efren Jimenez (c) Ismael Laguna

### 19. Jose Torres

(a) Roger Rouse (b) Don Fullmer (c) Gomeo Brennan

### 20. Jim Watt

(a) Jimmy Revie (b) Johnny Claydon (c) Borge Krogh

# WHAT YEAR WERE THEY BORN?

*In which year were the following boxers born?*

**1. Alexis Arguello**
(a) 1951 (b) 1952 (c) 1953

**2. Hogan Kid Bassey**
(a) 1932 (b) 1933 (c) 1934

**3. Nino Benvenuti**
(a) 1936 (b) 1937 (c) 1938

**4. Joe Calzaghe**
(a) 1972 (b) 1973 (c) 1974

**5. Chartchai Chionoi**
(a) 1941 (b) 1942 (c) 1943

**6. Chris Eubank**
(a) 1964 (b) 1965 (c) 1966

**7. Johnny Famechon**
(a) 1945 (b) 1946 (c) 1947

**8. Joe Frazier**
(a) 1943 (b) 1944 (c) 1945

**9. Rocky Graziano**
(a) 1919 (b) 1920 (c) 1921

**10. Paul Hodkinson**
(a) 1964 (b) 1965 (c) 1966

**11. Lloyd Honeyghan**
(a) 1960 (b) 1961 (c) 1962

**12. Pone Kingpetch**
(a) 1933 (b) 1934 (c) 1935

**13. Sonny Liston**
(a) 1930 (b) 1931 (c) 1932

**14. Charlie Magri**
(a) 1956 (b) 1957 (c) 1958

**15. Rocky Marciano**

(a) 1921 (b) 1922 (c) 1923

**16. Ruben Olivares**

(a) 1946 (b) 1947 (c) 1948

**17. Steve Robinson**

(a) 1966 (b) 1967 (c) 1968

**18. Lionel Rose**

(a) 1948 (b) 1949 (c) 1950

**19. Vicente Saldivar**

(a) 1942 (b) 1943 (c) 1944

**20. Mike Tyson**

(a) 1966 (b) 1967 (c) 1968

# NICKNAMES

*What are the nicknames of the following boxers?*

**1.  Henry Armstrong**
(a) The Chaser (b) Homicide Hank (c) Mr Knockout

**2.  Nigel Benn**
(a) Dark Destroyer (b) Terminator (c) Finisher

**3. Timothy Bradley Jr**
(a) Thunder (b) Desert Storm (c) Wild Wind

**4. Joe Brown**
(a) Old Bones (b) Sweet Dreams (c) The Finder

**5. Georges Carpentier**
(a) The Impossible (b) The Sender (c) The Orchid Man

**6. Lloyd Honeyghan**
(a) The Truth (b) Ragamuffin Man (c) Destroyer

**7. Lennox Lewis**
(a) The Lion (b) The Tiger (c) The Wolfe

**8. Joe Louis**
(a) The Sandman (b) The Brown Bomber (c) The Knockout Man

**9. Rocky Marciano**
(a) Dynamite (b) Mr Knockout (c) The Brockton Blockbuster

**10. Archie Moore**
(a) Old Mongoose (b) The Master (c) The Trickster

**11. Wayne McCullough**
(a) The Magic Man (b) The Believer (c) Pocket Rocket

**12. Barry McGuigan**
(a) The Clones Cyclone (b) The Irish Terror (c) The Breeze

**13. Azumah Nelson**
(a) The Student (b) The Professor (c) The Master

**14. Willie Pep**
(a) The Mover (b) Mr Boxing (c) Will o' the Wisp

**15. Aaron Pryor**

(a) The Hawk (b) The Eagle (c) The Kestrel

**16. Claressa Shields**

(a) The Flame (b) T-Rex (c) Golden Moments

**17. Josh Taylor**

(a) The Tartan Tornado (b) The Scottish Storm (c) The Scottish Terror

**18. Mike Tyson**

(a) Volcano Mike (b) Mike the Terminator (c) Iron Mike

**19. Dwight Muhammad Qawi**

(a) Camden Buzzsaw (b) Mr Busy (c) The King

**20. Tony Zale**

(a) Man of Truth (b) Man of Steel (c) Man of Iron

# MORE NICKNAMES

*Which boxers had the following nicknames?*

### 1. Bazooka
(a) Ruben Olivares (b) Wilfredo Gomez (c) Lionel Rose

### 2. Coalminer's Daughter
(a) Christy Martin (b) Mia St John (c) Jisselle Salandy

### 3. Chunky
(a) Robert Stieglitz (b) Mikkel Kessler (c) James DeGale

### 4. Dynamite
(a) Michael Dokes (b) Riddick Bowe (c) John Tate

### 5. Fighting Fireman
(a) Lonnie Smith (b) Kendall Holt (c) Terry Marsh

### 6. Golden Boy
(a) Hector Camacho (b) Oscar De La Hoya (c) DeMarcus Corley

### 7. Hi-Tech
(a) Vasiliy Lomachenko (b) Adrien Broner (c) Edwin Valero

### 8. Ice Man
(a) Simon Brown (b) Milton McCrory (c) Ike Quartey

### 9. Lights Out
(a) James Toney (b) Chris Eubank (c) Markcus Beyer

### 10. Little Red
(a) Sugar Ramos (b) Clemente Sanchez (c) Danny Lopez

### 11. Mundo
(a) Andre Ward (b) Callum Smith (c) Lucian Bute

### 12. One Time
(a) Keith Thurman (b) John H. Stracey (c) Jeff Horn

### 13. Pac-Man
(a) Freddie Norwood (b) Manny Pacquiao (c) Eloy Rojas

### 14. Paddington Express
(a) Terry Downes (b) Chris Pyatt (c) Alan Minter

### 15. Rapid Fire
(a) Tony Tucker (b) Chris Byrd (c) Ruslan Chagaev

### 16. The Rose of Soweto
(a) Dingaan Thobela (b) Brian Mitchell (c) Mzonke Fana

### 17. Saint George
(a) George Groves (b) Richie Woodhall (c) Glenn Catley

### 18. She Bee Stingin
(a) Elin Cederroos (b) Laila Ali (c) Nikki Adler

### 19. Sweet Pea
(a) Paul Spadafora (b) Jimmy Paul (c) Pernell Whitaker

### 20. Thunder
(a) Junior Witter (b) Arturo Gatti (c) Vivian Harris

# REAL NAMES

*What are the real names of the following boxers?*

### 1. Muhammad Ali
(a) Cassius Marcellus Clay (b) Lee Mackie (c) Dean Foster

### 2. Jack Kid Berg
(a) Philip Clayman (b) Judah Bergman (c) Morris Atwell

### 3. Tommy Burns
(a) Thomas Burnson (b) James Burnside (c) Noah Brusso

### 4. Joe Dundee
(a) Samuel Lazzara (b) Joey Goodrich (c) Bobby Perkins

### 5. Johnny Dundee
(a) John Freeman (b) Giuseppe Carrora (c) Carlos Santimore

### 6. Joey Giardello
(a) Joseph Pertain (b) Nino Carbella (c) Carmine Tilelli

### 7. Rocky Graziano
(a) Ricci Ribeiro (b) Thomas Rocco Barbella (c) Giancarlo Domenico Riozzi

### 8. Stanley Ketchel
(a) Luan Preberg (b) Alexis Secovic (c) Stanislaw Kiecal

### 9. Ted Kid Lewis
(a) Morris Andrews (b) Gershon Mendeloff (c) Teddy Silverman

### 10. Joey Maxim
(a) Giuseppe Antonio Berardinelli (b) Nino Carmile (c) Hansen Jordan

### 11. Archie Moore
(a) Bobby Scot (b) Archibald Lee Wright (c) Colin Bradley

### 12. Matthew Saad Muhammad
(a) Maxwell Antonio Loach (b) Crawford Dee Dixon (c) Mark Lee Johnson

### 13. Philadelphia Jack O'Brien
(a) Patrick Taylor Murphy (b) Michael Christopher Donovan (c) Joseph Francis Anthony Hagen

### 14. Willie Pep
(a) Gugliermo Papaleo (b) Nino Silverio (c) Pietro Salvatore

### 15. Eddie Babe Risko
(a) Peter Russo (b) Henry L. Pylkowski (c) Clement H. Parker

### 16. Sugar Ray Robinson
(a) Walker Smith Jr (b) Lonnie Johnson (c) Dwight Cranfield

### 17. Jack Sharkey
(a) Jimmy Croft (b) Benny Clark (c) Joseph Paul Zukauskas

### 18. Dick Tiger
(a) Richard Ihetu (b) Robert Bassey (c) Richard Fidde

### 19. Jersey Joe Walcott
(a)  Henry Adam Sanders (b) Arnold Raymond Cream (c) Freddie Lee Candale

### 20. Kid Williams
(a) Arthur Knight (b) Warren Cole (c) Jonathon Gutenko

# MIDDLE NAMES

*What are the middle names of the following boxers from the past and the present?*

### 1. Henry Akinwande
(a) Abasiofon (b) Adetokunboh (c) Abasifreke

### 2. Riddick Bowe
(a) Lamont (b) Clinton (c) Barclay

### 3. Shannon Briggs
(a) Patrick (b) Demont (c) Lionel

### 4. Jimmy Carruthers
(a) William (b) Nelson (c) Samuel

### 5. Ezzard Charles
(a) Mack (b) George (c) Clement

### 6. Jimmy Ellis
(a) Dennis (b) Albert (c) Calvin

### 7. Chris Eubank
(a) Livingstone (b) Gladstone (c) Winston

### 8. George Foreman
(a) John (b) Allen (c) Edward

### 9. Bob Foster
(a) Lloyd (b) Roger (c) Paul

### 10. Joe Frazier
(a) Robert (b) William (c) Colin

### 11. Carl Froch
(a) Martin (b) David (c) Lewis

### 12. Emile Griffith
(a) Wellington (b) Alphonse (c) Hector

### 13. Marvin Hagler
(a) Benjamin (b) Curtis (c) Nathaniel

### 14. Carlos Ortiz
(a) Juan (b) Miguel (c) Vincente

### 15. Shawn Porter
(a) Christian (b) George (c) Joseph

### 16. Lionel Rose
(a) Keith (b) Jeremy (c) Edmund

### 17. Callum Smith
(a) Malcolm (b) John (c) Alexander

### 18. Keith Thurman
(a) Martin (b) Wallace (c) Fitzgerald

### 19. Vic Toweel
(a) Ian (b) Anthony (c) Michael

### 20. Deontay Wilder
(a) Leshun (b) Franklin (c) Jordan

# MORE MIDDLE NAMES

*What are the middle names of the following boxers from both the past and the present?*

**1. Adrien Broner**
(a) Christopher (b) Dennis (c) Jerome

**2. Richard Commey**
(a) Clemente (b) Foster (c) Oblitey

**3. Terence Crawford**
(a) Allan (b) Steven (c) Claude

**4. Harry Greb**
(a) George (b) Henry (c) John

**5. James J. Jeffries**
(a) Jules (b) Jackson (c) Johnson

**6. Sugar Ray Leonard**
(a) Charles (b) Norman (c) Brian

**7. Lennox Lewis**
(a) Claudius (b) Julius (c) Markus

**8. Teofimo Lopez**
(a) Andres (b) Lara (c) Alvarez

**9. Tommy Loughran**
(a) Sean (b) Patrick (c) Shamus

**10. Oliver McCall**
(a) William (b) Robert (c) Steven

**11. Mike McCallum**
(a) McKenzie (b) McGowan (c) McNabb

**12. Charles Martin**
(a) David (b) Lee (c) Jeremy

**13. Tommy Morrison**
(a) David (b) Victor (c) Paul

**14. Caleb Plant**

(a) Hunter (b) Kane (c) Curtis

**15. Claressa Shields**

(a) Tina (b) Maria (c) Jennifer

**16.  James Smith**

(a) Odell (b) Ugas (c) Lubin

**17. Antonio Tarver**

(a) Reno (b) Deon (c) Neon

**18. Tony Tucker**

(a) Craig (b) Leonard (c) Walter

**19. Mike Tyson**

(a) Terence (b) Gerard (c) Paul

**20. Mike Weaver**

(a) Dennis (b) Dwayne (c) Vincent

# WHERE WERE THEY BORN?

*In which country were the following boxers born?*

**1. Horacio Accavallo**
(a) Mexico (b) Argentina (c) Venezuela

**2. Johnny Bredahl**
(a)  Denmark (b) Sweden (c) Norway

**3. Chucho Castillo**
(a) Philippines (b) Mexico (c) Spain

**4. Roberto Duran**
(a) Columbia (b) Panama (c) Puerto Rico

**5. Hiroyuki Ebihara**
(a)  Japan (b) China (c) Thailand

**6. Arturo Gatti**
(a) America (b) Italy (c) France

**7. Eder Jofre**
(a) Argentina (b) Philippines (c) Brazil

**8. Ingemar Johansson**
(a) Norway (b) Sweden (c) Denmark

**9. Donny Lalonde**
(a) America (b) Canada (c) Romania

**10. Cecilio Lastra**
(a) Spain (b) Italy (c) Nicaragua

**11. Jose Legra**
(a) Columbia (b) Cuba (c) Spain

**12. Carlos Monzon**
(a) Argentina (b) Romania (c) Slovenia

**13. Vincenzo Nardiello**
(a) Spain (b) Sweden (c) Germany

**14. Manny Pacquiao**
(a) Philippines (b) Nicaragua (c) Cuba

**15. James Page**

(a) America (b) England (c) Canada

**16. Vicente Rondon**

(a) Spain (b) Venezuela (c) America

**17. Mike Rossman**

(a) America (b) England (c) Australia

**18. Arnold Taylor**

(a) Guyana (b) Jamaica (c) South Africa

**19. Meldrick Taylor**

(a) America (b) Puerto Rico (c) Canada

**20. Kostya Tszyu**

(a) South Korea (b) Russia (c) Australia

# FIRST DEFEATS

*The following boxers were defeated for the first time in their professional careers by which opponent?*

**1. Muhammad Ali**
(a) Ken Norton (b) Joe Frazier (c) Larry Holmes

**2. Alexis Arguello**
(a) Omar Amaya (b) Oscar Espinosa (c) Jorge Reyes

**3. Ricky Burns**
(a) Terence Crawford (b) Alex Arthur (c) Carl Johanneson

**4. Marcel Cerdan**
(a) Victor Buttin (c) Cyrille Delannoit (c) Harry Craster

**5. John Conteh**
(a) Eddie Duncan (b) Mate Parlov (c) Matthew Saad Muhammad

**6. Hugo Corro**
(a) Norberto Rufino Cabrera (b) Vito Antuofermo (c) Hugo Inocencio Saavedra

**7. Victor Galindez**
(a) Juan Aguilar (b) Avenamar Peralta (c) Jorge Ahumada

**8. Ricky Hatton**
(a) Vyacheslav Senchenko (b) Floyd Mayweather Jr (c) Manny Pacquiao

**9. David Haye**
(a) Wladimir Klitschko (b) Carl Thompson (c) Tony Bellew

**10. Bernard Hopkins**
(a) Clinton Mitchell (b) Roy Jones Jr (c) Jermain Taylor

**11. Junior Jones**
(a) Kennedy McKinney (b) John Michael Johnson (c) Darryl Pinckney

**12. Wladimir Klitschko**
(a) Corrie Sanders (b) Lamon Brewster (c) Ross Puritty

**13. Sonny Liston**
(a) Muhammad Ali (b) Marty Marshall (c) Leotis Martin

### 14. Charlie Magri
(a) Juan Diaz (b) Jose Torres (c) Frank Cedeno

### 15. Johnny Nelson
(a) Magne Havnaa (b) Peter Brown (c) Tommy Taylor

### 16. Terry Norris
(a) Derrick Kelly (b) Joe Walker (c) Julian Jackson

### 17. Sandy Saddler
(a) Bobby McQuillar (b) Lou Alter (c) Jock Leslie

### 18. Mike Tyson
(a) Evander Holyfield (b) James Douglas (c) Lennox Lewis

### 19. Jim Watt
(a) Ken Buchanan (b) Willie Reilly (c) Victor Paul

### 20. Daniel Zaragoza
(a) Harold Petty (b) Miguel Lora (c) Jeff Fenech

# HOW MANY PROFESSIONAL BOUTS

*How many professional bouts did the following boxers have during their careers?*

**1. Henry Akinwande**
(a) 53 (b) 54 (c) 55

**2. Tim Austin**
(a) 30 (b) 31 (c) 32

**3. Ken Buchanan**
(a) 67 (b) 68 (c) 69

**4. Vuyani Bungu**
(a) 44 (b) 45 (c) 46

**5. Joe Calzaghe**
(a) 45 (b) 46 (c) 47

**6. Pat Clinton**
(a) 22 (b) 23 (c) 24

**7. Bob Foster**
(a) 63 (b) 64 (c) 65

**8. Kid Gavilán**
(a) 143 (b) 144 (c) 145

**9. Jeff Harding**
(a) 23 (b) 25 (c) 26

**10. Larry Holmes**
(a) 75 (b) 76 (c) 77

**11. Duilio Loi**
(a) 125 (b) 126 (c) 127

**12. Ricardo Lopez**
(a) 50 (b) 51 (c) 52

**13.Vincenzo Nardiello**
(a) 40 (b) 41 (c) 42

**14. Carlos Palomino**
(a) 36 (b) 37 (c) 38

**15. Floyd Patterson**

(a) 64 (b) 65 (c) 66

**16. Luis Rodriguez**

(a) 119 (b) 120 (c) 121

**17. Salvador Sanchez**

(a) 44 (b) 45 (c) 46

**18. Michael Spinks**

(a) 31 (b) 32 (c) 33

**19. John H. Stracey**

(a) 51 (b) 52 (c) 53

**20. Franco Udella**

(a) 41 (b) 42 (c) 43

# FIRST-ROUND VICTORIES

*How many first-round victories did the following boxers achieve during their professional careers?*

**1. Muhammad Ali**
(a) One (b) Two (c) Three

**2. Frank Bruno**
(a) 12 (b) 13 (c) 14

**3. Pipino Cuevas**
(a) Six (b) Seven (c) Eight

**4. Bobby Czyz**
(a) Four (b) Five (c) Six

**5. Chris Eubank**
(a) Four (b) Five (c) Six

**6. Bob Foster**
(a) Five (b) Six (c) Seven

**7. Arturo Gatti**
(a) 13 (b) 14 (c) 15

**8. Thomas Hearns**
(a) 10 (b) 11 (c) 12

**9. Jeff Lacy**
(a) Seven (b) Eight (c) Nine

**10. Sugar Ray Leonard**
(a) One (b) Two (c) Three

**11. Charlie Magri**
(a) Three (b) Four (c) Five

**12. Rocky Marciano**
(a) 10 (b) 11 (c) 12

**13. Jose Napoles**
(a) Eight (b) Nine (c) Ten

### 14. Ruben Olivares
(a) Seven (b) Eight (c) Nine

### 15. Aaron Pryor
(a) Three (b) Four (c) Five

### 16. Sugar Ray Robinson
(a) 19 (b) 20 (c) 21

### 17. Vicente Saldivar
(a) One (b) Two (c) Three

### 18. Johnny Tapia
(a) Seven (b) Eight (c) Nine

### 19. Felix Trinidad
(a) Seven (b) Eight (c) Nine

### 20. Tim Witherspoon
(a) 12 (b) 13 (c) 14

# BRITISH CHAMPIONS

*In which division did the following boxers win a British title?*

### 1. Eddie Avoth
(a) Heavyweight (b) Light-heavyweight (c) Middleweight

### 2. Andy Bell
(a) Super-flyweight (a) Bantamweight (c) Featherweight

### 3. Ensley Bingham
(a)  Welterweight (b) Super-welterweight (c) Middleweight

### 4. Johnny Cooke
(a) Lightweight (b) Welterweight (c) Middleweight

### 5. Maurice Cullen
(a) Lightweight (b) Super-lightweight (c) Welterweight

### 6. Alex Dickson
(a) Featherweight (b) Super-featherweight (c) Lightweight

### 7. Terry Dunstan
(a) Heavyweight (b) Light-heavyweight (c) Cruiserweight

### 8. Gordon Ferris
(a) Heavyweight (b) Light-heavyweight (c) Middleweight

### 9. Michael Gomez
(a) Featherweight (b) Super-featherweight (c) Lightweight

### 10. Charlie Hill
(a) Flyweight (b) Bantamweight (c) Featherweight

### 11. Mark Kaylor
(a) Middleweight (b) Super-middleweight (c) Light-heavyweight

### 12. Patrick Mullings
(a) Bantamweight (b) Super-bantamweight (c) Featherweight

### 13. Ian Napa
(a) Bantamweight (b) Super-bantamweight (c) Featherweight

### 14. Johnny Owen
(a) Flyweight (b) Bantamweight (c) Featherweight

### 15. Larry Paul
(a) Lightweight (b) Welterweight (c) Super-welterweight

### 16. Kostas Petrou
(a) Lightweight (b) Welterweight (c) Middleweight

### 17. Colin Powers
(a) Super-lightweight (b) Welterweight (c) Super-welterweight

### 18. Robbie Regan
(a) Flyweight (b) Bantamweight (c) Featherweight

### 19. David Starie
(a) Super-welterweight (b) Middleweight (c) Super-middleweight

### 20. Johnny Williams
(a) Heavyweight (b) Light-heavyweight (c) Middleweight

# COMMONWEALTH CHAMPIONS

*In which weight division did the following boxers win a Commonwealth title?*

### 1. Johnny Aba
(a) Super-featherweight (b) Lightweight (c) Welterweight

### 2. Evan Armstrong
(a) Flyweight (b) Bantamweight (c) Featherweight

### 3. Don Broadhurst
(a) Super-flyweight (b) Bantamweight (c) Super-bantamweight

### 4. Donovan Boucher
(a) Lightweight (b) Welterweight (c) Middleweight

### 5. Brian Carr
(a) Flyweight (b) Bantamweight (c) Super-bantamweight

### 6. Nedal Hussein
(a) Bantamweight (b) Super-bantamweight (c) Featherweight

### 7. Jawaid Khaliq
(a) Welterweight (b) Super-welterweight (c) Middleweight

### 8. Al Korovou
(a) Welterweight (b) Middleweight (c) Light-heavyweight

### 9. Steve Larrimore
(a) Lightweight (b) Super-lightweight (c) Welterweight

### 10. Alex Moon
(a) Bantamweight (b) Featherweight (c) Super-featherweight

### 11. Horace Notice
(a) Middleweight (b) Light-heavyweight (c) Heavyweight

### 12. Tony Oakey
(a) Middleweight (b) Light-heavyweight (c) Heavyweight

### 13. Nicky Piper
(a) Middleweight (b) Super-middleweight (c) Light-heavyweight

### 14. Johnny Pritchett
(a) Welterweight (b) Middleweight (c) Light-heavyweight

**15. Apollo Sweet**

(a) Middleweight (b) Light-heavyweight (c) Cruiserweight

**16. Johnson Tishuma**

(a) Welterweight (b) Middleweight (c) Light-heavyweight

**17. Tommy Waite**

(a) Flyweight (b) Bantamweight (c) Featherweight

**18. Guy Waters**

(a) Middleweight (b) Light-heavyweight (c) Heavyweight

**19. Richard Williams**

(a) Super-lightweight (b) Welterweight (c) Super-welterweight

**20. Leo Young Jr**

(a) Welterweight (b) Super-welterweight (c) Middleweight

# EUROPEAN CHAMPIONS

*In which weight division did the following boxers win a European title?*

**1. Spend Abazi**
(a) Bantamweight (b) Featherweight (c) Lightweight

**2. Wayne Alexander**
(a) Welterweight (b) Super-welterweight (c) Middleweight

**3. Johnny Armour**
(a) Flyweight (b) Bantamweight (c) Featherweight

**4. Mimoun Chent**
(a) Flyweight (b) Bantamweight (c) Featherweight

**5. Yawe Davis**
(a) Middleweight (b) Light-heavyweight (c) Heavyweight

**6. Alfredo Evangelista**
(a) Middleweight (b) Light-heavyweight (c) Heavyweight

**7. Bruno Girard**
(a)  Middleweight (b) Super-middleweight (c) Light-heavyweight

**8. Alexander Gurov**
(a) Light-heavyweight (b) Cruiserweight (c) Heavyweight

**9. Carlos Hernandez**
(a) Featherweight (b) Super-featherweight (c) Lightweight

**10. Jesper Jensen**
(a) Flyweight (b) Bantamweight (c) Featherweight

**11. Martin Krastev**
(a) Bantamweight (b) Super-bantamweight (c) Featherweight

**12.  Jan Lefeber**
(a) Middleweight (b) Light-heavyweight (c) Heavyweight

**13. Kirkland Laing**
(a) Welterweight (b) Super-welterweight (c) Middleweight

**14. Christian Merle**
(a) Lightweight (b) Super-lightweight (c) Welterweight

### 15. Antonio Puddu
(a) Lightweight (b) Welterweight (c) Super-welterweight

### 16. Frederic Seillier
(a) Middleweight (b) Super-middleweight (c) Light-heavyweight

### 17. Mamadou Thiam
(a) Welterweight (b) Super-welterweight (c) Middleweight

### 18. Peter Waterman
(a) Lightweight (b) Welterweight (c) Middleweight

### 19. Lorenzo Zanon
(a) Middleweight (b) Light-heavyweight (c) Heavyweight

### 20. Alexander Zaytsev
(a) Middleweight (b) Light-heavyweight (c) Heavyweight

# WORLD CHAMPIONS

*In which weight division did the following boxers win a version of the world title?*

**1. Anatoly Alexandrov**
(a) WBC featherweight (b) WBO super-featherweight (c) WBA lightweight

**2. Bernard Benton**
(a) IBF middleweight (b) WBA super-middleweight (c) WBC cruiserweight

**3. Berkrerk Chartvanchai**
(a) WBA flyweight (b) WBC bantamweight (c) WBA featherweight

**4. Curtis Cokes**
(a) WBC lightweight (b) Undisputed welterweight (c) Undisputed middleweight

**5. Eckhard Dagge**
(a) WBC lightweight (b) Undisputed welterweight (c) WBC super-welterweight.

**6. Jimmy Ellis**
(a) WBA middleweight (b) WBA light-heavyweight (c) WBA heavyweight

**7. Sixto Escobar**
(a) Undisputed bantamweight (b) Undisputed featherweight (c) undisputed lightweight

**8. Hilmer Kenty**
(a) WBC featherweight (b) WBA lightweight (c) WBC super-lightweight

**9. Dado Marino**
(a) Undisputed flyweight (b) Undisputed bantamweight (c) Undisputed featherweight

**10. Johnny Nelson**
(a) WBO light-heavyweight (b) WBO cruiserweight (c) IBF heavyweight

**11. Fulgencio Obelmejias**
(a) WBC welterweight (b) IBF middleweight (c) WBA super-middleweight

**12. Joey Olivo**
(a) WBA light-flyweight (b) WBC bantamweight (c) IBF super-bantamweight

**13. Yober Ortega**
(a) WBC super-flyweight (b) IBF bantamweight (c) WBA super- bantamweight

### 14. Payao Poontarat
(a) WBA flyweight (b) WBC super-flyweight (c) IBF bantamweight

### 15. Jake Rodriguez
(a) WBC lightweight (b) IBF super-lightweight (c) WBA welterweight

### 16. Maxie Rosenbloom
(a) Undisputed middleweight (b) Undisputed light-heavyweight (c) Undisputed heavyweight

### 17. Randolph Turpin
(a) Undisputed welterweight (b) Undisputed middleweight (c) Undisputed light-heavyweight

### 18. Mike Weaver
(a) WBC middleweight (b) WBA light-heavyweight (c) WBA heavyweight

### 19. Jimmy Wilde
(a) Undisputed flyweight (b) Undisputed bantamweight (c) Undisputed featherweight

### 20. Fritzie Zivic
(a) Undisputed lightweight (b) Undisputed welterweight (c) Undisputed middleweight

# IN WHICH WEIGHT DIVISION?

*In which weight division did the following boxers not hold a world title?*

### 1. Carmen Basilio
(a) Undisputed lightweight (b) Undisputed middleweight (c) Undisputed welterweight

### 2. Nigel Benn
(a) WBC super-middleweight (b) WBO middleweight (c) WBA super-welterweight

### 3. Nino Benvenuti
(a) WBA super-welterweight (b) Undisputed light-heavyweight (c) Undisputed middleweight

### 4. Steve Collins
(a) WBO light-heavyweight (b) WBO middleweight (c) WBO super-middleweight

### 5. Donald Curry
(a) WBA super-lightweight (b) Undisputed welterweight (c) WBC super-welterweight

### 6. Chris Eubank
(a) WBO super-middleweight (b) WBO light-heavyweight (c) WBO middleweight

### 7. Fighting Harada
(a) Undisputed bantamweight (b) Undisputed flyweight (c) Undisputed featherweight

### 8. Ricky Hatton
(a) WBC lightweight (b) WBA welterweight (c) WBA & IBF super-lightweight

### 9. Evander Holyfield
(a) Undisputed cruiserweight (b) Undisputed light-heavyweight (c) Undisputed heavyweight

### 10. Julian Jackson
(a) WBA super-welterweight (b) WBC middleweight (c) WBC super-middleweight

### 11. Eder Jofre
(a) Undisputed bantamweight (b) WBC featherweight (c) Undisputed flyweight

### 12. Santos Laciar
(a) WBA flyweight (b) WBA bantamweight (c) WBC super-flyweight

### 13. Michael Moorer
(a) WBC middleweight (b) WBO IBF WBA heavyweight (c) WBO light-heavyweight

### 14. Azumah Nelson
(a) WBC lightweight (b) WBC super-featherweight (c) WBC featherweight

### 15. Ruben Olivares
(a) WBA & WBC featherweight (b) WBA flyweight (c) Undisputed bantamweight

### 16. Sugar Ray Robinson
(a) Undisputed welterweight (b) Undisputed middleweight (c) Undisputed light-heavyweight

### 17. Kuniaki Shibata
(a) WBC featherweight (b) WBA lightweight (c) WBA & WBC super-featherweight

### 18. Michael Spinks
(a) IBF heavyweight (b) WBC middleweight (c) Undisputed light-heavyweight

### 19. Lupe Pintor
(a) WBC bantamweight (b) WBC flyweight (c) WBC super-bantamweight

### 20. Paul Weir
(a) WBO minimumweight (b) WBO light-flyweight (c) WBO Flyweight

# NAME THE REFEREE

*Name the referee of the following world title contests:*

*1. On 20 December 1905, when Philadelphia Jack O'Brien won the world light-heavyweight crown and holder Bob Fitzsimmons retired in round 13.*
(a) Charlie White (b) John Duffy (c) Eddie Graney

*2. When Tommy Burns retained the world heavyweight crown on 17 March 1908 after he knocked out challenger Jem Roche in the first round.*
(a) Robert P. Watson (b) Eddie Robinson (c) Charles Eyton

*3. When Stanley Ketchel remained world middleweight champion on 31 July 1908 after he ended the challenge of Hugo Kelly by a knock out in round three.*
(a) Jack Welsh (b) Billy Roche (c) James J. Jeffries

*4. When Jack Britton retained the world welterweight title on 7 February 1921 after he outpointed former champion Ted Kid Lewis over 15 rounds.*
(a) Patsy Haley (b) Harry Stout (c) Dick Nugent.

*5. When Jack Dempsey retained the world heavyweight championship on 14 September 1923 after he knocked out challenger Luis Angel Firpo in round two.*
(a) Harry Ertle (b) Johnny Gallagher (c) Johnny Haukop

*6. On 19 December 1924 when Eddie Martin became the new world bantamweight champion after he outpointed holder Abe Goldstein over 15 rounds.*
(a) Tommy Sheridan (b) Patsy Haley (c) Lou Magnolia

*7. When the world welterweight title changed hands on 3 June 1927 after Joe Dundee outpointed defending champion Pete Latzo over 15 rounds.*
(a) Eddie Forbes (b) Jack Dorman (c) Toby Irwin

*8. When John Henry Lewis remained the world light-heavyweight champion after he outpointed challenger Jock McAvoy over 15 rounds on 13 March 1936.*
(a) Jack Smith (b) Arthur Donovan (c) Walter Heisner

*9. When Ike Williams retained his NBA world lightweight title on 4 September 1946 after he knocked out challenger Ronnie James in round nine.*
(a) Charley Randolph (b) Moss Deyong (c) Benny Whitman

*10. When Jimmy Carruthers won the world and commonwealth bantamweight crown on 15 November 1952 after he knocked out holder Vic Toweel in the first round.*
(a) Vic Patrick (b) Willie Smith (c) Jack English

**11. On 6 June 1958 when Virgil Akins won the vacant world welterweight crown after he knocked out opponent Vince Martinez in round four.**

(a) Lee Grossman (b) Ray Barnes (c) Harry Kessler

**12. When Hogan Kid Bassey made a successful defence of his world featherweight title on 1 April 1958 after he knocked out challenger Ricardo Moreno in round three.**

(a) Tommy Hart (b) Al Berl (c) Frankie Van

**13. When Flash Elorde retained his world super-featherweight crown after he outpointed challenger Johnny Bizzarro over 15 rounds in a contest that took place on 16 February 1963.**

(a) Felipe Hernandez (b) Irineo Gallegos (c) Jaime Valencia

**14. When Pone Kingpetch became a former champion when challenger Salvatore Burruni outpointed him over 15 rounds on 23 April 1965 to become the new world flyweight title holder.**

(a) Ramon Berumen (b) Harry Gibbs (c) Harold Valan

**15. When Muhammad Ali remained the world heavyweight champion on 25 May 1965 after he knocked out Sonny Liston in the first round.**

(a) Jackie Silvers (b) Barney Felix (c) Jersey Joe Walcott

**16. When world light-heavyweight champion Bob Foster made short work of his challenger Frank DePaula on 22 January 1969 after disposing of him by way of a knockout in round one.**

(a) Mark Conn (b) Johnny LoBianco (c) Lee Sala

**17. When Denny Moyer failed in his challenge for the world middleweight championship on 4 March 1972 when defending title holder Carlos Monzon stopped him in round five.**

(a) Harry Gibbs (b) Victor Avendano (c) Lorenzo Fortunato

**18. When Wilfredo Gomez kept hold of his WBC world super- bantamweight title on 28 September 1979 after he stopped challenger Carlos Mendoza in round ten.**

(a) Arthur Mercante (b) Richard Green (c) Joey Curtis

**19. When Rafael Pedroza became the new WBA world super-flyweight champion on 5 December 1981 after he outpointed holder Gustavo Ballas over 15 rounds.**

(a) Solomon Allen (b) Rudy Jordan (c) Larry Rozadilla

**20. On 5 May 1984 when WBA world cruiserweight champion Ossie Ocasio turned back the challenge of John Odhiambho after he stopped him in round 15.**

(a) Isidro Rodriguez (b) Carlos Berrocal (c) John Coyle

# MORE NAME THE REFEREE

*Name the referee of the following world title contests:*

*1. When Tommy Loughran retained his world light-heavyweight title on 28 March 1929 after he outpointed challenger Mickey Walker over ten rounds.*
(a) Eddie Forbes (b) Davy Miller (c) Leo Houck

*2. When Joe Louis remained king of the heavyweight division on 28 June 1939 when he successfully retained his world title stopping Tony Galento in round four.*
(a) Arthur Donovan (b) Sam Hennessey (c) Johnny Martin

*3. When Terry Downes won the New York and European version of the world middleweight crown on 11 July 1961 after holder Paul Pender retired in round nine.*
(a) Tommy Little (b) Jack Hart (c) Ike Powell

*4. When Walter McGowan boxed his way to a 15-round point's decision on 14 June 1966 to take the Lineal, European and British world flyweight versions of the crown from holder Salvatore Burruni. (Prior to meeting McGowan, Burruni had been stripped of both the WBA and WBC versions of the title.)*
(a) Ike Powell (b) Harry Gibbs (c) Bill Williams

*5. When Jose Napoles confirmed his position as the top man in his division on 14 December 1971 when he retained his world welterweight crown, outpointing challenger Hedgemon Lewis over 15 rounds.*
(a) Larry Rozadilla (b) Jay Edson (c) Octavio Meyran

*6. On 30 April 1976 when Muhammad Ali turned back the challenge of Jimmy Young by way of a 15-round point's decision to retain the world heavyweight championship.*
(a) Takeo Ugo (b) Harry Cecchini (c) Tom Kelly

*7. When Marvin Hagler brought an end to the challenge of Mustafa Hamsho by a stoppage in round 11 on 3 October 1981 to retain his world middleweight title.*
(a) Octavio Meyran (b) Stanley Christodoulou (c) Ernesto Magana

*8. When Aaron Pryor remained the WBA world super-lightweight champion on 14 November 1981 after he stopped challenger Dujuan Johnson in round seven.*
(a) Mills Lane (b) Jackie Keough (c) Roberto Ramirez Sr

*9. On 15 March 1983, when Charlie Magri won the WBC world flyweight title stopping defending champion Eleoncio Mercedes in round seven.*
(a) Angelo Poletti (b) Ray Solis (c) Marty Denkin

**10. When Livingstone Bramble stopped his challenger Tyrone Crawley in round 13 on 16 February 1986 in defence of his WBA world lightweight championship.**

(a) Joe Cortez (b) Mills Lane (c) Joey Curtis

**11. When Virgil Hill retained his WBA world light-heavyweight crown on 3 April 1988 after he stopped challenger Jean-Marie Emebe in round 11.**

(a) Steve Smoger (b) Roberto Ramirez Snr (c) Hubert Earle

**12. When Alfred Cole kept the world IBF cruiserweight title when he stopped his challenger Vincent Boulware in five rounds on 17 November 1993.**

(a) Robert Palmer (b) Tony Orlando (c) Rafael Ramos

**13. When the WBC world middleweight crown remained in the hands of defending champion Gerald McClellan on 4 March 1994 when he stopped his challenger Gilbert Baptist in the first round.**

(a) Tony Perez (b) Richard Steele (c) Mills Lane

**14. When Steve Robinson confirmed his position as a major player in the featherweight division on 4 February 1995 after he made a successful defence of his WBO world crown, outpointing challenger Domingo Nicolas Damigella over 12 rounds.**

(a) Toby Gibson (b) Ismael Wiso Fernandez (c) Roy Francis

**15. When Luis Ramon Campas lost the IBF world super-welterweight crown on 12 December 1998 after retiring in round seven against challenger Fernando Vargas.**

(a) Joe Cortez (b) James Condon (c) Eddie Cotton

**16. On 22 October 2004, when defending holder Joe Calzaghe retained his WBO world super-middleweight title, outpointing challenger Kabary Salem over 12 rounds.**

(a) Paul Thomas (b) Dave Parris (c) Mark Nelson

**17. When Junior Witter retained his WBC world super-lightweight championship on 7 September 2007, knocking out challenger Vivian Harris in round seven.**

(a) Timothy Adams (b) Massimo Barrovecchio (c) Daniel Van de Wiele

**18. When Mia St John won the vacant WBC world female super-welterweight title on 14 August 2012, outpointing opponent Christy Martin over ten rounds.**

(a) Marcos Rosales (b) Jose Guadalupe Garcia (c) Stefano Carozza

**19. When Errol Spence Jr became the new IBF world welterweight champion on 27 May 2017, knocking out title holder Kell Brook in round 11.**

(a) Steve Gray (b) Howard Foster (c) Marlon Wright

**20. When Charlie Edwards boxed his way to a 12-round point's decision to win the WBC world flyweight title on 22 December 2018, defeating defending champion Cristofer Rosales.**

(a) Mark Lyson (b) Victor Loughlin (c) Ian John Lewis

# WHICH COUNTRY?

*In which country did the following fighters not box during their professional careers?*

**1. Alexis Arguello**

(a) Japan (b) America (c) Spain

**2. Salvatore Burruni**

(a) Canada (b) Japan (c) Australia

**3. Primo Carnera**

(a) France (b) England (c) Sweden

**4. John Conteh**

(a) Demark (b) Italy (c) America

**5. Chris Eubank**

(a) Egypt (b) America (c) Spain

**6. Johnny Famechon**

(a) South Africa (b) America (c) England

**7. Bob Foster**

(a) Denmark (b) Germany (c) South Africa

**8. Joe Frazier**

(a) England (b) Australia (c) Italy

**9. Fighting Harada**

(a) Thailand (b) Australia (c) England

**10. Maurice Hope**

(a) Spain (b) America (c) Germany

**11. Tom Johnson**

(a) England (b) Australia (c) Denmark

**12. Glenn McCrory**

(a) Russia (b) Denmark (c) Italy

**13. Walter McGowan**

(a) America (b) Italy (c) Thailand

**14. Carlos Monzon**

(a) France (b) England (c) Italy

### 15. Jose Napoles
(a) Italy (b) England (c) Japan

### 16. Carlos Ortiz
(a) England (b) Italy (c) Canada

### 17. Robin Reid
(a) Germany (b) America (c) South Africa

### 18. Sugar Ray Robinson
(a) Japan (b) Germany (c) France

### 19. Vicente Saldivar
(a) Italy (b) Brazil (c) Spain

### 20. Jim Watt
(a) America (b) Spain (c) Nigeria

# HOW TALL?

*The 20 listed boxers all held a version of the world heavyweight title during their careers, but how tall were they?*

**1. Muhammad Ali**
(a) 6ft 1in (b) 6ft 2in (c) 6ft 3in

**2. Max Baer**
(a) 6ft 2 ½in (b) 6ft 3in (c) 6ft 4in

**3. Michael Bentt**
(a) 6ft 2in (b) 6ft 3in (c) 6ft. 4in

**4. Riddick Bowe**
(a) 6ft 5in (b) 6f 6in (c) 6ft 7in

**5. Lamon Brewster**
(a) 6f 1in (b) 6ft 2in (b) 6ft 3in

**6. Tommy Burns**
(a) 5ft 7in (b) 5ft 8in (c) 5ft 9in

**7. Ezzard Charles**
(a) 5ft 11in (b) 6ft (c) 6ft 1in

**8. Francesco Damiani**
(a) 6ft 1in (b) 6ft 2in (c) 6ft 3in

**9. George Foreman**
(a) 6ft 3in (b) 6ft 4in (c) 6ft 5in

**10. Joe Frazier**
(a) 5ft 11½ in (b) 6f 1in (b) 6ft 2in

**11. Herbie Hide**
(a) 6ft (b) 6ft 1in (c) 6ft 2in

**12. Sonny Liston**
(a) 6ft 1in (b) 6ft 2in (c) 6ft 3in

**13. Ray Mercer**
(a) 5ft 11in (b) 6ft (c) 6ft 1in

**14. Ken Norton**

(a) 6ft 3in (b) 6ft 4in (c) 6ft 5in

**15. Floyd Patterson**

(a) 5ft 11in (b) 6ft (c) 6ft 1in

**16. Leon Spinks**

(a) 6ft 1in (b) 6ft 2in (c) 6ft 3in

**17. Pinklon Thomas**

(a) 6ft 2in (b) 6ft 3in (c) 6ft 4in

**18. Tony Tubbs**

(a) 6ft 1in (b) 6ft 2in (c) 6ft 3in

**19. Mike Tyson**

(a) 5ft 10in (b) 5ft 11in (c) 6ft

**20. Tim Witherspoon**

(a) 6ft 2in (b) 6ft 3½in (c) 6ft 4in

# MEDAL WINNERS AT THE OLYMPIC GAMES

*The Olympic Games through the years have seen many exceptional fighters perform well enough to attain a much-desired medal. Many medal winners go on to replicate their success in the paid ranks. Below are are questions about the boxing in the Olympics.*

*1. In the 1904 Games held in St. Louis, USA Oliver Kirk won gold medals in two weight divisions – bantamweight and featherweight. What was his nationality?*
(a)  American (b) Canadian (c) Australian

*2. Which Briton won the gold medal in the heavyweight division at the 1908 games held in London, England?*
(a) Sydney Evans (b) Albert Oldman (c) Frederick Parks

*3. In the 1920 Games, which were held in Antwerp, Belgium, American Frankie Genaro won a gold medal in which weight division?*
(a) Flyweight (b) Bantamweight (c) Featherweight

*4. At the 1924 Games staged in Paris, France Harry Mallin (GB) won which colour medal in the Middleweight division?*
(a) Bronze (b) Silver (c) Gold

*5. How many gold medals did Italy win at the 1928 Games, which took place in Amsterdam, Holland?*
(a) One (b) Two (c) Three

*6. At the 1932 games held in Los Angeles, USA, Hungary's Istvan Enekes won a gold medal in which weight division?*
(a) Flyweight (b) Bantamweight (c) Featherweight

*7. What colour medal did Roger Michelot of France win in the light-heavyweight division at the 1936 Berlin, West Germany, Games?*
(a) Bronze (b) Silver (c) Gold

*8. Hungary's Laszlo Papp won a gold medal in which weight division at the 1948 London, England, Games?*
(a) Welterweight (b) Middleweight (c) Heavyweight

*9. At the 1952 Games held in Helsinki, Finland, who won the gold medal in the middleweight division?*
(a) Floyd Patterson (America) (b) Vasile Tita (Romania) (c) Boris Nikolov (Bulgaria)

**10. In which weight division did Terry Spinks (GB) win a gold medal at the 1956 Games held in Melbourne, Australia?**

(a) Flyweight (b) Bantamweight (c) Featherweight

**11. Which colour medal did Italy's Nino Benvenuti win in the welterweight division in the 1960 games held in Rome, Italy?**

(a) Bronze (b) Silver (c) Gold

**12. Who won the gold medal in the heavyweight division at the 1964 Games held in Tokyo, Japan?**

(a) Hans Huber (Germany) (b) Joe Frazier (America) (c) Vadim Yemelyanov (Soviet Union)

**13. At the 1968 Games held in Mexico City, Mexico, Chris Finnegan (GB) won a gold medal in which weight division?**

(a) Middleweight (b) Light-heavyweight (c) Heavyweight

**14. Teofilo Stevenson won three consecutive gold medals in the heavyweight division. Stevenson claimed the first medal at the 1972 Games, which took place in Munich, West Germany. The second medal came in 1976 when the event took place in Montreal, Canada, and finally the third medal became his at the 1980 Moscow, USSR, Games. What was the nationality of Stevenson?**

(a) Panamanian (b) American (c) Cuban

**15. How many gold medals did America win at the 1984 games staged in Los Angeles, America?**

(a) Eight (b) Nine (c) Ten

**16. At the 1988 Seoul, South Korea, Games, East German Henry Maske won which colour medal in the middleweight division?**

(a) Bronze (b) Silver (c) Gold

**17. At the 1992 Barcelona, Spain, 1996 Atlanta, USA, and 2000 Sydney, Australia, Games, Felix Savon of Cuba won gold medals in which weight division?**

(a) Light-heavyweight (b) Heavyweight (c) Super-heavyweight

**18. Who won the gold medal in the lightweight division at the 2004 Games, which took place in Athens, Greece?**

(a) Amir Khan (GB) Mario Kindelan (Cuba) Serik Yeleuov (Kazakhstan)

**19. At the 2008 Games held in Beijing, China, Vasiliy Lomachenko of the Urkraine won a gold medal in the featherweight division. In the 2012 Games, which took place in London, England, he won a second gold in which weight division?**

(a) Featherweight (b) Lightweight (c) Welterweight

**20. Tony Yoka won a gold medal in the super-heavyweight division at the 2016 Games, which were held in Rio de Janeiro, Brazil. What was his nationality?**

(a) Canadian (b) Belgium (c) French

ROUND TWENTY-FIVE

# FILMS

*There have been a number of films made over the years which have been based on the fight game or indeed have had boxers play a role in various productions. The following questions are about those films.*

**1. In the film** Gentleman Jim **(1942), Errol Flynn played the part of James J. Corbett. Which actor took the role of John L. Sullivan?**
(a) Ward Bond (b) Alan Hale Jr (c) Victor McLaglen

**2. The film** Emergency Call **(1952) starred Jack Warner and featured which boxer who participated in the light-heavyweight division in the role of Tim Mahoney?**
(a) Joey Maxim (b) Gus Lesnevich (c) Freddie Mills

**3. A** Kid for Two Farthings **(1955) starred Celia Johnson and featured former world heavyweight champion Primo Carnera, who played the part Python Macklin. What was Macklin's sporting occupation in the film?**
(a) Footballer (b) Boxer (c) Wrestler

**4. Which former British and Commonwealth heavyweight champion made an appearance in the film** All for Mary **(1955), which starred Nigel Patrick?**
(a) Jack Petersen (b) Tommy Farr (c) Jack London

**5. The film** The Harder They Fall **(1956) starred Humphrey Bogart and featured which former world heavyweight champion in the role of George?**
(a) Jersey Joe Walcott (b) Joe Louis (c) Ezzard Charles

**6. The film** Somebody up There Likes Me **(1956) Starred Paul Newman, who portrayed which former world middleweight champion?**
(a) Tony Zale (b) Rocky Graziano (c) Gene Fullmer

**7.** Up Pompeii **(1971) was a comedy film that starred Frankie Howerd and featured which former heavyweight boxer who was cast as Prodigious?**
(a) Johnny Prescott (b) Billy Walker (c) Billy Gray

**8.** Royal Flash **(1975) was a film that starred Malcolm McDowell and featured former British European and Commonwealth heavyweight champion Henry Cooper, but who played the role of which old-time fighter?**
(a) John Gully MP (b) Tom Allen (c) Jem Smith

**9. The film** Breakheart Pass **(1975) starred Charles Bronson and featured which former world light-heavyweight champion in the role of Carlos?**
(a) Joey Maxim (b) Harold Johnson(c) Archie Moore

*10. Mandingo (1975) was a film that starred James Mason. Which boxer, who had achieved high honours in the heavyweight division, played the part of Mede?*
(a) Ken Norton (b) Larry Holmes (c) Muhammad Ali

*11. Sylvester Stallone starred in the film Rocky (1976). Which former world heavyweight champion made an appearance?*
(a) George Foreman (b) Joe Frazier (c) Floyd Patterson

*12. Raging Bull (1980) was a film that starred Robert De Niro playing the role of which former World middleweight champion?*
(a) Carl Bobo Olson (b) Jake LaMotta(c) Joey Giardello

*13. Rocky V (1990) saw Sylvester Stallone reprise the role of Rocky Balboa. Who was the future world-title holder who played the part of Tommy 'The Machine' Gunn in the film?*
(a) Sultan Ibragimov (b) Corrie Sanders (c) Tommy Morrison

*14. The film The Hurricane (1999) saw actor Denzel Washington playing the role of which former boxer?*
(a) Rubin Carter (b) Tom Bethea (c) Bennie Briscoe

*15. The film Ali (2001) saw Will Smith take on the role of Muhammad Ali. Which former WBO world heavyweight champion played the part of Sonny Liston?*
(a) Ray Mercer (b) Henry Akinwande (c) Michael Bentt

*16. The Clint Eastwood film Million Dollar Baby (2004) featured which female boxer in the role of Billie?*
(a) Lucia Rijker (b) Diana Dutra (c) Carla Witherspoon

*17. Cinderella Man (2005) was a film which saw Russell Crowe in the leading role. Which former World heavyweight Champion was the film based on?*
(a) Jack Sharkey (b) Max Baer (c) James J. Braddock

*18. The Hangover (2009), a comedy starring Bradley Cooper, was a film that featured an appearance from which former world heavyweight champion?*
(a) Mike Tyson (b) Lennox Lewis (c) George Foreman

*19. The Fighter (2010) was a film based on the life of boxer Micky Ward. Which actor played the role of Ward?*
(a) Christian Bale (b) Mark Wahlberg (c) Ben Affleck

*20. Creed (2015) saw Michael B. Jordan play the title role. Who was the future world-title holder who played the part of 'Pretty' Ricky Conlan?*
(a) Mairis Briedis (b) Oleksandr Usyk (c) Tony Bellew

# MORE FILMS

*A further 20 questions based on films that have a boxing theme or a boxer playing a part.*

**1.** On the Waterfront *(1954) Starred Marlon Brandon as ex-boxer Terry Malloy. Which former world heavyweight title challenger appeared in the film as Barney?*
(a) Abe Simon (b) Tami Mauriello (c) Buddy Baer

**2.** Utah Blaine *(1957) was a western that had Rory Calhoun in the title role. The cast included which former world heavyweight champion playing the part of Gus Ortmann?*
(a) Primo Carnera (b) Max Baer (c) Max Schmeling

**3.** All the Young Men *(1960) saw Alan Ladd in the leading role as Private Kincaid. Which boxer played the part of Private Torgil?*
(a) Rocky Marciano (b) Floyd Patterson (c) Ingemar Johansson

**4.** In Kid Galahad *(1962) Elvis Presley played the part of Walter Gulick. Former boxer Mushy Callahan appeared as a referee. In which weight division had Callahan once reigned as a world-title holder?*
(a) Lightweight (b) Super-lightweight (c) Welterweight

**5.** The Carpet Baggers *(1964) starred George Peppard as Jonas Cord. Which former world light-heavyweight title holder played the part of Jedediah?*
(a) Archie Moore (b) Harold Johnson (c) Joey Maxim

**6.** Harlow *(1965), based on the legendary actress Jean Harlow, starred Caroll Baker in the leading role. Which former world heavyweight champion made an appearance in the film?*
(a) Floyd Patterson (b) Sonny Liston (c) Ingemar Johansson

**7.** In the film Tony Rome *(1967), Frank Sinatra played the title role. Which former world middleweight champion had the part of a character called Packy in the production?*
(a) Rocky Graziano (b) Terry Downes (c) Paul Pender

**8.** Candy *(1968) Starred Ewa Aulin in the lead role. Which former world champion played Zero?*
(a) Sugar Ray Robinson (b) Gene Fullmer (c) Carl Bobo Olson

**9.** Up the Chastity Belt *(1971) was a comedy film that starred Frankie Howerd, who played the role of both Lurkalot andRichard the Lionheart. Which former boxer appeared in the production playing the part of Chopper?*
(a) Brian London (b) Billy Walker (c) Billy Gray

**10.** *Farewell My Lovely (1975) saw Robert Mitchum play the part of Philip Marlowe. Which former heavyweight boxer played the role of Moose Malloy?*
(a) Scott Frank (b) Jack O'Halloran (c) George Chuvalo

**11.** *Drum (1976) had Warren Oates playing the part of Hammond Maxwell. Which former holder of a world heavyweight title played the role of Drum?*
(a) Floyd Patterson (b) Ernie Terrell (c) Ken Norton

**12.** *Superman (1978) saw Christopher Reeve playing the man of steel with which former heavyweight boxer in the role of Non?*
(a) Jack O'Halloran (b) Billy Walker (c) Ron Stander

**13.** *The Godfather Part III (1990) saw Al Pacino in the role of Michael Corleone. Which former world middleweight champion played the part of Anthony Squigliaro?*
(a) Vito Antuofermo (b) Nino Benvenuti (c) Hugo Corro

**14.** *Ace Ventura: Pet Detective (1994) Starred Jim Carrey in the lead role. Who was the former heavyweight boxer who appeared in the cast?*
(a) Jack O' Halloran (b) Chuck Wepner (c) Randall 'Tex' Cobb

**15.** *Ocean's Eleven (2001) saw George Clooney play the part of Danny Ocean. Which two fighters were seen boxing each other in the film?*
(a) Lennox Lewis v Michael Moorer (b) Lennox Lewis v Wladimir Klitschko (c) Lennox Lewis v Frank Bruno

**16.** *Alexander (2004) had Colin Farrell starring in the title role. Which former British super-welterweight champion appeared as Cleitus the Black?*
(a) Andy Till (b) Gary Cooper (c) Gary Stretch

**17.** *Rocky Balboa (2006) had Sylvester Stallone once again reprising the role of Rocky. Which boxer who achieved world-title status at light-heavyweight during his career appeared in the part of Mason 'The Line' Dixon?*
(a) Antonio Tarver (b) Glen Johnson (c) Chad Dawson

**18.** *Night at The Museum: Battle of The Smithsonian (2009) saw Ben Stiller once again playing the part of Larry Daley. Which former world heavyweight title holder made an appearance in the film?*
(a) Lennox Lewis (b) George Foreman (c) Frank Bruno

**19.** *In the film Risen (2010), Stuart Brennan played the part of which former world boxing champion?*
(a) Howard Winstone (b) Jimmy Wilde (c) Robbie Regan

**20.** *Hands of Stone (2016) starred Edgar Ramirez in the role of which boxer?*
(a) Carlos Ortiz (b) Roberto Duran (c) Mando Ramos

# FIND THE SOUTHPAW

*One fighter in each line below fought in the southpaw stance. Can you identify the fighter from the past or present who boxed in that stance in each set of three. (Note: A boxer who fights in this stance leads with his right hand and right foot forward.)*

1. (a) Cornelius Boza-Edwards (b) Alexis Arguello (c) Ray Mancini

2. (a) Jeff Lacy (b) Joe Calzaghe (c) Steve Collins

3. (a) Tomasz Adamek (b) Virgil Hill (c) Chad Dawson

4. (a) James DeGale (b) Chris Eubank (c) George Groves

5. (a) Carl Froch (b) Andre Dirrell (c) Jose Uzcategui

6. (a) Mickey Walker (b) Harry Greb (c) Tiger Flowers

7. (a) Krzysztof Glowacki (b) Krzysztof Wlodarczyk (c) Enzo Maccarinelli

8. (a) Julian Jackson (b) Marvin Hagler (c) Shinji Takehara

9. (a) Terry Norris (b) Koichi Wajima(c) Maurice Hope

10. (a) Zab Judah (b) Meldrick Taylor (c) Pedro Adigue Jr.

11. (a) Vitali Tajbert (b) Rafael Limon (c) Regilio Tuur

12. (a) Sergio Martinez (b) Julio Cesar Chavez Jr. (c) Felix Sturm

13. (a) Carlos Monzon (b) James Toney (c) Alan Minter

14. (a) Tim Witherspoon (b) Michael Moorer (c) Henry Akinwande.

15. (a) Manny Pacquiao (b) Shane Mosley (c) Paulie Malignaggi

16. (a) Terry Allen (b) Benny Lynch (c) Jackie Paterson

17. (a) Sandy Saddler (b) Willie Pep (c) Vicente Saldivar

18. (a) Samuel Peter (b) Corrie Sanders (c) Lamon Brewster

19. (a) Billy Joe Saunders (b) Arthur Abraham (c) Emile Griffith

20. (a) John Conteh (b) Bob Foster (c) Adonis Stevenson

# WOMEN IN BOXING

*Twenty questions based on the women who have made a contribution to the sport.*

*1. Who was the first woman to be appointed as a boxing judge in America in 1973?*
(a) Eva Shain (b) Carol Polis (c) Patricia Morse Jarman

*2. On 29 September 1977 Muhammad Ali defended his world heavyweight title against challenger Earnie Shavers and retained his crown by way of a 15-round points decision. For the first time in the history of the sport a woman judge presided at ringside for a world heavyweight championship bout, but who was it?*
(a) Carol Polis (b) Eva Shain (c) Lynne Carter

*3. Who was the first female to be given a professional boxing licence by the British Boxing Board of Control*
(a) Jan Wild (b) Juliette Winter (c) Jane Couch

*4. Riddick Bowe made a successful defence of his WBA world heavyweight championship on 22 May 1993 when challenger Jesse Ferguson was knocked out in round two. All three judges in attendance at ringside were women. Two of them were Sheila Harmon and Patricia Morse Jarman, but who was the third official?*
(a) Debra Barnes (b) Lynne Carter (c) Eugenia Williams

*5. Who in 1993 became Britain's first corner-woman?*
(a) Tania Follett (b) Lisa Budd (c) Annette Conroy

*6. Vonda Ward became the first holder of the Women's WBC world heavyweight championship on 10 February 2007 when she defeated opponent Martha Salazar, but by which method?*
(a) Four-round knockout (b) Eight-round stoppage (c) Ten-round points decision.

*7. What was Ward's middle name?*
(a) Julie (b) Anne (c) Kaye

*8. In which year did Jane Couch receive the MBE?*
(a) 2007 (b) 2008 (c) 2009

*9. Which one of the following boxed in the orthodox stance?*
(a) Laila Ali (b) Mary Ann Almager (c) Holly Holm

*10. Who became the first female administrative stewart for the British Boxing Board of Control?*
(a) Katherine Morrison (b) Tania Follett (c) Judith Rollestone

*11. Savannah Marshall became the first British female to win a gold medal at the 2012 AIBA world championships which were held in Qinhuangdao, China. In which weight division did Marshall compete?*
(a) Welterweight (b) Middleweight (c) Light-heavyweight

*12. Which one of the following box in the southpaw stance?*
(a) Chantelle Cameron (b) Natasha Jonas (c) Katie Taylor

*13. What is the nickname of Cecilia Braekhus?*
(a) First Lady (b) Top lady (c) Boss Lady

*14. Kristen Fraser became the first holder of the Commonwealth female bantamweight crown on 24 November 2018 when she defeated opponent Ellen Simwaka for the vacant title, but by which method?*
(a) Three-round knockout (b) Five-round retirement (c) Eight-round knockout

*15. In which year was Cecilia Braekhus born?*
(a) 1981 (b) 1982 (c) 1983

*16. What is the nationality of Katie Taylor?*
(a) Irish (b) Scottish (c) Welsh

*17. How tall is Claressa Shields?*
(a) 5ft 6in (b) 5ft 7in (c) 5ft 8in

*18. In which capacity is Verity Panter involved with boxing?*
(a) Master of ceremonies (b) Referee (c) Judge

*19. Which boxer is nicknamed The Baby Faced Assassin?*
(a) Ashley Brace (b) Kristen Fraser (c) Shannon Courtenay

*20. Who, in 2020, became the first woman to become the honorary secretary of the Commonwealth Boxing Council?*
(a) Tania Follett (b) Debbie Down (c) Miranda Carter

# BOXING BROTHERS

*The listed 20 boxers also had brothers who fought in the ring. Find their first name from the selection provided.*

*1. Muhammad Ali*
(a) Rahman (b) Jarrah (c) Shakan

*2. Max Baer*
(a) Johnny (b) Bobby (c) Buddy

*3. Orlando Canizales*
(a) Sergio (b) Gaby (c) Roberto

*4. Donald Curry*
(a) Bruce (c) David (c) Bobby

*5. Anthony Dirrell*
(a) Derry (b) Andre (c) Bernard

*6. Nonito Donaire*
(a) Glenn (b) Paul (c) Frankie

*7. Gene Fullmer*
(a) Barry (b) Sammy (c) Don

*8. Mikey Garcia*
(a) Robert (b) Davey (c) Javier

*9. Arturo Gatti*
(a) Alex (b) Carlos (c) Joe

*10. Ricky Hatton*
(a) Philip (b) Matthew (c) Jonas

*11. Amir Khan*
(a) Haroon (b) Vikram (c) Kunal

*12. Jake LaMotta*
(a) Lee (b) Denny (c) Joey

*13. Danny Lopez*
(a) Bobby (b) Ernie (c) Jason

**14. Milton McCrory**

(a) Steve (b) Brian (c) Chris

**15. Terry Norris**

(a) Brady (b) Jack (c) Orlin

**16. Floyd Patterson**

(a) Larry (b) Ray (c) Alan

**17. Michael Spinks**

(a) Leon (b) Foster (c) Ray

**18. Tony Tubbs**

(a) Terry (b) Nate (c) Jermain

**19. Fernando Vargas**

(a) Rogelio (b) Rafael (c) Julio

**20. Deontay Wilder**

(a) Gerald (b) Mateo (c) Marsellos

# WORLD CHAMPIONSHIP CONTESTS

*In which country did the following world championship contests take place?*

*1. On 3 September 1908 where did Tommy Burns have a successful night after he knocked out challenger Bill Lang in round six to retain his world heavyweight crown?*
(a) Canada (b) Australia (c) America

*2. Where did Harry Greb retain his world middleweight title when he turned back the challenge of Fay Keiser on 24 March 1924 by a stoppage in round 12?*
(a) France (b) Philippines (c) America

*3. Where did Panama Al Brown keep hold of the world bantamweight title on 10 July 1932, outpointing challenger Kid Francis over 15 rounds?*
(a) Italy (b) France (c) Spain

*4. Where did Freddie Miller retain his NBA world featherweight crown on 12 June 1935 when he outpointed challenger Nel Tarleton over the duration of 15 rounds?*
(a) England (b) America (c) Canada

*5. On 5 October 1952 where id Kid Gavilan retain the world welterweight championship when he outpointed challenger Billy Graham over 15 rounds?*
(a) America (b) South Africa (c) Cuba

*6. Where did Paddy DeMarco become the new world lightweight champion on 5 March 1954 when he outpointed reigning title holder Jimmy Carter over 15 rounds?*
(a) Japan (b) America (c) Italy

*7. Where did Sugar Ramos retain the world featherweight title on 1 March 1964 when he terminated the challenge of Mitsunori Seki by a stoppage in round six?*
(a) Japan (b) Mexico (c) Venezuela.

*8. Where did Carmelo Bossi became the new WBA super-welterweight champion of the world on the 9 July 1970 when he outpointed holder Freddie Little over the duration of 15 rounds?*
(a) America (b) Spain(c) Italy

*9. Where did Venice Borkhorsor win the WBC world flyweight crown on 29 September 1972 when defending champion Betulio Gonzalez was stopped in round ten?*
(a) Japan (b) Argentina (c) Thailand

10. *Where did Muhammad Ali retain the world heavyweight championship on 24 May 1976 when he stopped challenger Richard Dunn in round five?*

(a) England (b) Germany (c) South Africa

11. *Where did the WBC world featherweight title change hands on 6 November 1976 when Danny Lopez outpointed defending title holder David Kotey over 15 rounds?*

(a) Ghana (b) South Korea (c) Italy

12. *On 12 March 1977, where did Pipino Cuevas retain his WBA world welterweight crown, knocking out challenger Miguel Angel Campanino in round two.*

(a) America (b) Mexico (c) Canada

13. *Where was a new WBA world heavyweight champion crowned on 20 October 1979 when John Tate outpointed Gerrie Coetzee over 15 rounds for the vacant title?*

(a) South Africa (b) America (c) Italy

14. *On 18 July 1986, where did Gilberto Roman retained his WBC world super-flyweight title, outpointing challenger Ruben Condori over 12 rounds?*

(a) Mexico (b) Cuba (c) Argentina

15. *Where did Chong-Pal Park make a successful defence of his IBF world super-middleweight title on 3 May 1987 when he outpointed challenger Lindell Holmes over 15 rounds?*

(a) South Korea (b) Japan (c) America

16. *On 18 October 1989, where did Luisito Espinosa win the WBA world bantamweight championship when he knocked defending title-holder Khaokor Galaxy in the first round?*

(a) Australia (b) Thailand (c) Switzerland

17. *Where did Luis Mendoza retain his WBA world Super-bantamweight crown on 30 May 1991, knocking out challenger Joao Cardoso in round seven?*

(a) Denmark (b) Mexico (c) Spain

18. *Where did Chris Pyatt contest the vacant WBO world middleweight crown on 19 May 1993 and emerge as the new title holder when he outpointed opponent Sumbu Kalambay over 12 rounds?*

(a) England (b) Nigeria (c) Italy

19. *Where did Stefania Bianchini win the vacant WBC world female flyweight title on 7 August 2005 when she outpointed Cathy Brown over ten rounds?*

(a) France (b) Spain (c) Italy

20. *On 29 December 2007, where did Steve Cunningham retained the IBF world cruiserweight title when he stopped challenger Marco Huck in round 12?*

(a) America (b) Germany (c) Austria

# MORE WORLD CHAMPIONSHIP CONTESTS

*In which country did the following world championship contests take place?*
*1. The 27 June 1914 fight in which Jack Johnson maintained his position as the world heavyweight champion when he outpointed challenger Frank Moran over the duration of 20 rounds.*
(a) America (b) Canada (c) France

*2. The fight in which Henry Armstrong confirmed his claim of being the best welterweight around at the time by successfully defending his world title by stopping his challenger Bobby Pacho in round four in a contest that took place on 4 March 1939.*
(a) America (b) Cuba (c) Mexico

*3. The fight in which Tirso Del Rosario failed to capture the world bantamweight title on 20 December 1947 when title holder Manuel Ortiz outpointed him over 15 rounds.*
(a) Philippines (b) Argentina (c) France

*4. The 11 November 1953 fight when Jimmy Carter retained his world lightweight championship, knocking out challenger Armand Savoie in round five?*
(a) America (b) Spain (c) Canada

*5. The match that saw Joe Brown turn back the challenge of Dave Charnley on 18 April 1961, defeating him by way of a 15-round points decision when defending the world lightweight crown.*
(a) America (b) England (c) Germany

*6. The match that saw Floyd Patterson retain the world heavyweight crown on 4 December 1961 in empathic style when he knocked out challenger Tom McNeeley in round four.*
(a) Canada (b) America (c) Sweden

*7. The 5 June 1971 match that saw Vicente Rondon make quick work of his challenger when defending his WBA world light-heavyweight title, knocking out Piero Del Papa in the first round.*
(a) Italy (b) Venezuela (c) Brazil

*8. The fight in which Carlos Monzon retained the world middleweight championship on 19 August 1972, stopping challenger Tom Bogs in round five.*
(a) Argentina (b) France (c) Denmark

*9. The fight in which Netrnoi Sor Vorasingh won the WBC world light-flyweight crown on 6 May 1978 when he outpointed the defending champion Freddy Castillo over 15 rounds.*

(a) Mexico (b) Thailand (c) America

*10. The fight that saw the IBF world cruiserweight championship change hands on 25 October 1986 when challenger Rickey Parkey stopped defending title-holder Lee Roy Murphy in round ten.*

(a) Spain (b) France (c) Italy

*11. The match that saw Jeff Lampkin keep the IBF world cruiserweight championship on 28 July 1990 when challenger Siza Makathini was knocked out in the eighth round.*

(a) America (b) Denmark (c) Sweden

*12. The fight that saw Tim Austin retain his IBF world bantamweight title, stopping his challenger Paul Lloyd in the second round in a contest that took place on 28 March 1998.*

(a) England (b) America (c) Italy

*13. The fight in which Naseem Hamed retained his WBO world featherweight championship on the 31 October 1998, outpointing his challenger Wayne McCullough over 12 rounds.*

(a) America (b) England (c) Mexico

*14. The world WBO super-featherweight championship fight that came to a close on 26 October 1999 in the second round when title holder Acelino Freitas stopped challenger Anthony Martinez.*

(a) Brazil (b) Cuba (c) Canada

*15. The match that saw Masibulele Makepula capture the vacant WBO world light-flyweight championship when outpointing opponent Jacob Matlala over 12 rounds on 19 February 2000.*

(a) Australia (b) New Zealand (c) South Africa

*16. The 13 October 2001 fight that saw Joe Calzaghe retain his WBO world super-middleweight title, stopping challenger Will McIntyre in round four.*

(a) Denmark (b) England (c) America

*17. The fight in which Oscar Larios retained his WBC world super-bantamweight title on 7 September 2003, stopping his challenger Kozo Ishii in the second round.*

(a) Mexico (b) Japan (c) Austria

*18. The 16 October 2010 fight in which Vitali Klitschko outpointed his challenger Shannon Briggs over 12 rounds to retain his WBC world heavyweight championship.*

(a) Germany (b) America (c) Canada

*19. The fight that saw Carl Froch emerge victorious when he outpointed opponent Arthur Abraham on 27 November 2010 to win the vacant WBC world super-middleweight crown.*

(a) Norway (b) Denmark (c) Finland

*20. The fight in which Robert Stieglitz held on to his WBO world super-middleweight title when he outpointed his challenger Nader Hamdan over 12 rounds on 5 May 2012.*

(a) Austria (b) Germany (c) Sweden

# PROMOTERS AND MANAGERS

*The following is a list of boxing promoters and managers from the past to the present. Do you know their first names?*

**1. Arum**
(a) Steve (b) Bob (c) Paul

**2. Barrett**
(a) Mike (b) Alan (c) Bennie

**3. DiBella**
(a) Dave (b) Danny (c) Lou

**4. Duff**
(a) Daniel (b) Mickey (c) Stanley

**5. Eastwood**
(a) Colin (b) Angus (c) Barney

**6. Eaton**
(a) Aileen (b) Elizabeth (c) Sarah

**7. Follett**
(a) Tina (b) Tania (c) Anne

**8. Hearn**
(a) Benjamin (b) Harry (c) Barry

**9. Hearn**
(a) Eddie (b) Brian (c) Terry

**10. Hennessy**
(a) Jack (b) Mick (c) Gary

**11. Kallen**
(a) Jackie (b) Paula (c) Linda

**12. King**
(a) Peter (b) Don (c) Bobby

**13. Lawless**
(a) Terry (b) Ian (c) David

### 14. Levene
(a) Bradley (b) Harry (c) Robert

### 15. Maloney
(a) Kellie (b) Julie (c) Sandra

### 16. Palle
(a) Kurt (b) Mogens (c) Karl

### 17. Rickard
(a) Jack (b) Tex (c) Clinton

### 18. Solomons
(a) Jack (b) Morris (c) Sidney

### 19. Warren
(a) Paul (b) Frank (c) David

### 20. Wicks
(a) Jim (b) Dennis (c) Phillip

# MORE PROMOTERS AND MANAGERS

*The following is a list of boxing promoters and managers from the past to the present. Do you know their first names?*

**1. Astaire**
(a) Jack (b) Jarvis (c) Kenneth

**2. Baker**
(a) Timmy (b) Johnny (c) Bruce

**3. Biddles**
(a) Lennard (b) George (c) Claude

**4. Black**
(a) Julian (b) Lee (c) Harry

**5. Boggis**
(a) David (b) George (c) Arthur

**6. Broadribb**
(a) Johnny (b) Ted (c) George

**7. Carter**
(a) Jenny (b) Patricia (c) Miranda

**8. Demmy**
(a) Gus (a) James (c) Ian

**9. Gibbons**
(a) Brian (b) Tommy (c) Clive

**10. Griffiths**
(a) Tommy (b) Alex (c) Ben

**11. Helliet**
(a) Lawrence (b) Charles (c) Mickey

**12. Hobson**
(a) Dennis (b) Ray (c) Kenneth

**13. Holland**
(a) Paul (b) Dennis (c) Harry

**14. Jacobs**
(a) Mike (b) Christopher (c) Ronald

### 15. Kearns
(a) John (b) Benny (c) Jack

### 16. Kushner
(a) Cedric (b) Alan (c) Clive

### 17. Middleton
(a) Henry (b) Brian (c) George

### 18. Morrison
(a) Katherine (b) Carole (c) Mary

### 19. Roxborough
(a) Maurice (b) John (c) Nigel

### 20. Sanigar
(a) Paul (b) Chris (c) Neville

# PHOTOGRAPH QUIZ

*Can you name the following boxers (a clue is under each respective image)?*

(Photo Derek Rowe)

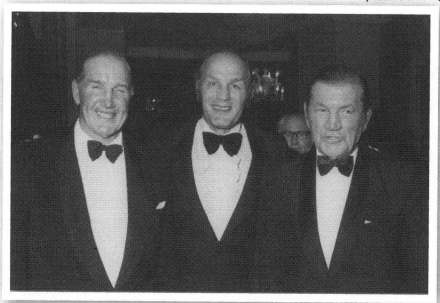

*1. Left of photo is Jack Petersen in the centre is Henry Cooper. Who is the former boxer on the right? He lost a 15-round points decision on 30 August 1937 when he challenged Joe Louis for the world heavyweight title.*

(Photo Derek Rowe)

*2. On the right of photo is Pat Dwyer and on the left is a former world heavyweight champion. He won the crown on 23 September 1952, knocking out defending title holder Jersey Joe Walcott in round 13.*

**3. This boxer made history when he became the first fighter to regain the world heavyweight championship on 20 June 1960, knocking out former conqueror Ingemar Johansson in round five.**

(Photo Derek Rowe)

**4. He won the British middleweight title on 8 November 1965 when stopping defending champion Wally Swift in round 12.**

(Photo Derek Rowe)

*5. He became the new British flyweight champion when knocking out opponent Tony Barlow in round eight to win the vacant crown on 16 January 1967.*

*6. This boxer won the vacant WBC world featherweight title on 23 January 1968, stopping opponent Mitsunori Seki in round nine.*

*7. He won the British and Commonwealth middleweight titles on 12 May 1970 when stopping defending champion Les McAteer in round 14.*

*8. A former world champion who lost his last professional contest on 30 July 1977, losing a ten-round points decision to Alan Minter.*

9. *He won the British heavyweight title and twice held the WBO world heavyweight championship during his professional career.*

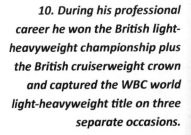

10. *During his professional career he won the British light-heavyweight championship plus the British cruiserweight crown and captured the WBC world light-heavyweight title on three separate occasions.*

(Photo Les Clark)

*11. He won the WBC version of the world heavyweight championship on 22 November 1986, stopping defending title holder Trevor Berbick in two rounds.*

*12. He boxed his way to a 12-round point's decision on 16 May 1992 to take the WBO world featherweight title from holder Maurizio Stecca.*

(Photo Les Clark)

*13. He won the WBC world bantamweight championship when outpointing defending title holder Yasuei Yakushiji over 12 rounds on 30 July 1995.*

*14. He stopped defending champion Steve Robinson in round eight on 30 September 1995 to win the WBO world featherweight title.*

*15. On 12 October 1996 he became the new WBC world super-middleweight champion when stopping the defending title holder Vincenzo Nardiello in round seven.*

*16. He captured the IBF world bantamweight championship on 19 July 1997, stopping defending title holder Mbulelo Botile in round eight.*

*17. He became the WBO world cruiserweight title holder when he outpointed defending champion Ralf Rocchigiani on 4 October 1997 over the duration of 12 rounds.*

*18. He won the IBF world featherweight title on 13 November 1999 when outpointing the reigning champion Manuel Medina over 12 rounds.*

(Photo Les Clark)

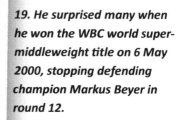

*19. He surprised many when he won the WBC world super-middleweight title on 6 May 2000, stopping defending champion Markus Beyer in round 12.*

*20. Before going on to win world honours in two weight divisions, he won the vacant British super-lightweight crown on 21 October 2000 when outpointing Jon Thaxton over 12 rounds.*

(Photo Philip Sharkey)

# MORE PHOTOGRAPHS

*1. On the left of photo is Sugar Ray Robinson, but who is the boxing manager on the right who took a number of fighters to the world, European, Commonwealth and British titles during his duration in the sport?*

(Photo Derek Rowe)

(Photo Derek Rowe)

*2. He failed in his bid to win the world welterweight championship on 22 September 1964 when outpointed over 15 rounds by defending title holder Emile Griffith.*

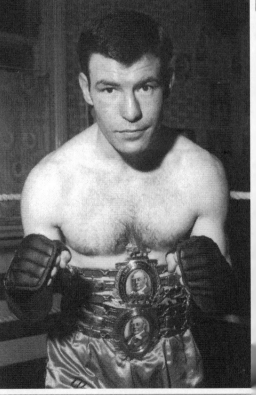

*3. Against the odds, he took the WBA world lightweight title from the reigning champion Ismael Laguna on 26 September 1970, outpointing him over 15 rounds.*

*4. He filled the vacancy for the WBC world light-heavyweight championship on 1 October 1974 when he won the title, outpointing opponent Jorge Ahumada over the duration of 15 rounds.*

*5. He won the WBC world welterweight championship on 6 December 1975, stopping defending title holder Jose Napoles in round six.*

*6. He won the world middleweight title on 16 March 1980, outpointing defending champion Vito Antuofermo over 15 rounds.*

*7. His challenge for the WBA world featherweight championship proved successful on 8 June 1985 when holder Eusebio Pedroza was outpointed over 15 rounds.*

*8. During his professional career he won the world British European and Commonwealth welterweight titles, plus the Commonwealth super-welterweight crown.*

*9. This boxer took the IBF world super-lightweight championship from the reigning title holder Joe Manley on 4 March 1987 with a stoppage in round ten.*

10. *During his professional career he won the British, Commonwealth and European super-welterweight titles, plus the British and European middleweight titles.*

11. *He had his last professional contest in America on 21 June 2003, stopping challenger Vitali Klitschko in round six in defence of his WBC and IBO world heavyweight titles.*

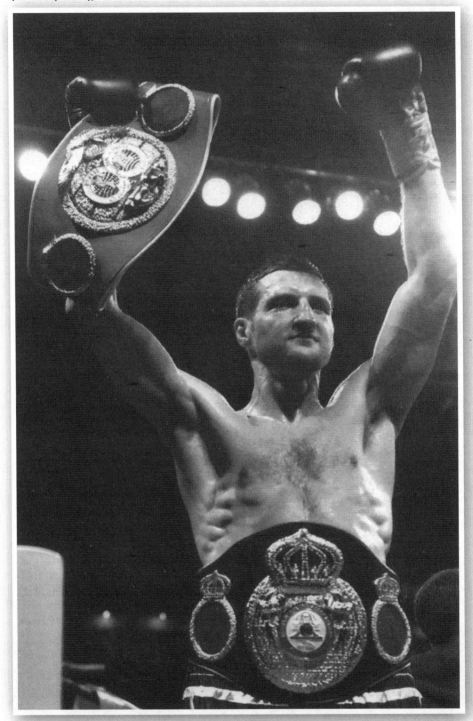

*12. He defeated Jean Pascal by way of a 12-round points decision on 6 December 2008 to win the vacant WBC world super-middleweight title.*

*13. He made a successful bid for the WBA world super-lightweight crown on 18 July 2009, outpointing defending champion Andriy Kotelnik over 12 rounds.*

*14. During his professional career he won the European cruiserweight crown plus the WBA super version of the world cruiserweight crown and the WBC, and WBO world cruiserweight titles and added to his championship tally by winning the WBA world heavyweight crown.*

*15. He remained WBO world light-heavyweight champion when outpointing challenger Tony Bellew over 12 rounds on 15 October 2011.*

(Photo Philip Sharkey)

*16. He won the IBF world middleweight crown on 17 August 2013 when outpointing defending champion Daniel Geale over 12 rounds.*

*17. The boxer on left of the photo is Gennady Golovkin. Who is the fighter on the right who won the IBF world welterweight championship on 16 August 2014, outpointing the defending title holder Shawn Porter over 12 rounds?*

(Photo Philip Sharkey)

*18. He won the IBF world super-bantamweight title on 6 September 2014, outpointing holder Kiko Martinez over 12 rounds.*

*19. He captured the IBF world featherweight title on 30 May 2015 when defeating the defending champion Evgeny Gradovich by an eight-round technical decision.*

*20. He defended the WBC diamond super-middleweight title and won the WBA super world super-middleweight championship on 28 September 2018 by knocking out holder George Groves in round seven.*

# GENERAL KNOWLEDGE QUIZ

*1. On 17 March 1897, Bob Fitzsimmons won the world heavyweight title when he knocked out holder James J. Corbett in which round?*
(a) 12 (b) 13 (c) 14

*2. Who was the referee of the Fitzsimmons-Corbett title contest?*
(a) George Siler (b) Charlie White (c) Eddie Graney

*3. On 11 October 1899 Joe Gans outpointed opponent Martin Judge over how many rounds?*
(a) 10 (b) 15 (c) 20

*4. Jack Johnson retained his world heavyweight title on 16 October 1909 when he knocked out which challenger in round 12?*
(a) James J. Jeffries (b) Fireman Jim Flynn (c) Stanley Ketchel

*5. Jimmy Wilde opposed Dick Jenkins on 9 March 1911 and won by which method?*
(a) Six-round points decision (b) Eight-round points decision (c) Ten-round points decision.

*6. Where in the United Kingdom was Jimmy Wilde born?*
(a)  Scotland (b) Wales (c) England

*7. On 26 July 1923 Johnny Dundee won the world featherweight title when he outpointed holder Eugene Criqui over 15 rounds. Where in the USA was the venue for this contest?*
(a) Polo Grounds, New York (b) Madison Square Garden, New York (c) Velodrome, New York

*8. Who was the referee of the Dundee-Criqui title contest?*
(a) Slim Brennan (b) Patsy Haley (c) Jack O' Sullivan

*9. Tiger Flowers captured the world middleweight crown on 26 February 1926 when he defeated holder Harry Greb by a 15-round points decision. In which country did this contest take place?*
(a) Canada (b) America (c) Panama

*10. On 28 September 1928 Andre Routis fought his way to a 15-round points decision when capturing the world featherweight crown from holder Tony Canzoneri. In which country did this contest take place?*
(a) America (b) France (c) Canada

**11. Prior to winning the title, Andre Routis had participated in how many professional contests?**

(a) 76 (b) 77 (c) 78

**12. Who was the referee of the Routis-Canzoneri title contest?**

(a) Bill Conway (b) Eddie Forbes (c) Harry Ertle

**13. On 3 September 1930, Jack Kid Berg retained the NBA version of the world super-lightweight crown when he outpointed challenger Buster Brown over how many rounds?**

(a) 10 (b) 12 (c) 15

**14. In which country did the Berg-Brown title contest take place?**

(a) England (b) Canada (c) America

**15. On 29 June 1933, Primo Carnera won the world heavyweight title when he knocked out holder Jack Sharkey in which round?**

(a) Five (b) Six (c) Seven

**16. Who was the referee of the Carnera-Sharkey title contest?**

(a) Leo Shea (b) Roger Nicod (c) Arthur Donovan

**17. Joe Louis stopped opponent Hans Birkie in which round on 11 January 1935?**

(a) Eight (b) Nine (c) Ten

**18. Who was the referee of the Louis-Birkie contest?**

(a) Davy Miller (b) Red Robinson (c) Tommy Gilmore

**19. At this stage of his career Joe Louis was now undefeated in how many professional contests?**

(a) 12 (b) 13 (c) 14

**20. On 2 October 1935 George Daly defeated opponent Seaman Tommy Watson by which method?**

(a) One-round stoppage (b) Eight-round retirement (c) Nine-round knockout

**21. Seaman Tommy Watson was a former British champion in which weight division?**

(a) Bantamweight (b) Featherweight (c) Lightweight

**22. Henry Armstrong won the world lightweight title on 17 August 1938 when he defeated holder Lou Ambers by which method?**

(a) Six-round disqualification (b) Nine-round stoppage (c) 15-round points decision.

**23. At the time of the Armstrong-Ambers world title contest, who was the reigning British lightweight champion?**

(a) Eric Boon (b) Dave Crowley (c) Jimmy Walsh

**24. On 15 September 1944, Jack London won the vacant British and Commonwealth heavyweight titles when he outpointed which opponent over 15 rounds?**

(a) Ken Shaw (b) Freddie Mills (c) George James

**25. Who had relinquished those titles prior to Jack London capturing them?**

(a) Len Harvey (b) Tommy Farr (c) Ben Foord

**26. On 28 August 1946 Joey Maxim outpointed Jersey Joe Walcott over how many rounds?**

(a) 10 (b) 12 (c) 15

**27. Who was the referee of the Maxim-Walcott contest?**

(a) Lou Mauder (b) Lou Scozza (c) Paul Cavalier

**28. Rocky Graziano failed in his challenge for the world middleweight crown on 27 September 1946 when he was knocked out by defending champion Tony Zale in which round?**

(a) Five (b) Six (c) Seven

**29 Who was the referee of the Zale-Graziano title contest?**

(a) Ruby Goldstein (b) Barney Ross (c) Johnny Behr

**30. How many bouts had Rocky Graziano participated in prior to his challenge for Tony Zale's middleweight title?**

(a) 52 (b) 53 (c) 54

**31. Sandy Saddler won the vacant world super-featherweight championship on 6 December 1949 when he outpointed Orlando Zulueta over ten rounds. Who was the previous holder of the title?**

(a) Frankie Klick (b) Kid Chocolate (c) Benny Bass

**32. Sandy Saddler had previously held a world championship in which other weight division?**

(a) Flyweight (b) Bantamweight (c) Featherweight

**33. Jack Gardner won the European heavyweight title on 27 March 1951 when he defeated holder Jo Weidin by which method?**

(a) Six-round knockout (b) Nine-round stoppage (c) 15-round points decision.

**34. What was the nationality of Jo Weidin?**

(a) German (b) Austrian (c) French

**35. The vacant world bantamweight championship was filled on 19 September 1954 when Robert Cohen defeated opponent Chamroen Songkitrat by which method?**

(a) Two-round stoppage (b) Six-round knockout (c) 15-round points decision

**36. Who was the referee of the Cohen-Songkitrat title contest?**

(a) Wilf Lubbe (b) Teddy Waltham (c) Rene Schemann

**37. In which country did the Cohen-Songkitrat title contest take place?**

(a) Thailand (b) France (c) England

**38. Who was the holder of the world bantamweight title prior to the victor of the Cohen-Songkitrat contest?**

(a) Manuel Ortiz (b) Jimmy Carruthers (c) Vic Toweel

**39. Rocky Marciano successfully defended his world heavyweight title on 21 September 1955 when he knocked out challenger Archie Moore in which round?**

(a) Seven (b) Eight (c) Nine

**40. Prior to delivering the knockout, Rocky Marciano was floored for a count by Archie Moore in which round?**

(a) One (b) Two (c) Three

**41. Who was the referee of the Marciano-Moore title contest?**

(a) Harry Kessler (b) Frank Sikora (c) Charley Daggert

**42. Where in the USA was the venue for the Marciano-Moore title contest?**

(a) Madison Square Garden, New York (b) Yankee Stadium, Bronx, New York (c) Kezar Stadium, San Francisco, California

**43. Soon after the Archie Moore victory, Rocky Marciano retired from the sport having made how many successful defences of the world heavyweight title?**

(a) Six (b) Seven (c) Eight

**44. Rocky Marciano retired from boxing with an undefeated record of how many bouts?**

(a) 47 (b) 48 (c) 49

**45. Henry Cooper and Heinz Neuhaus fought over ten rounds on 11 January 1958. What was the result?**

(a) A win for Cooper on points (b) A draw (c) A win for Neuhaus on points

**46. In which country did the Cooper-Neuhaus contest take place?**

(a) England (b) Austria (c) Germany

**47. Heinz Neuhaus was a former European champion in which weight division?**
(a) Middleweight (b) Light-heavyweight (c) Heavyweight

**48. Henry Cooper had participated in how many professional contests prior to his meeting with Heinz Neuhaus?**
(a) 21 (b) 22 (c) 23

**49. Heinz Neuhaus had participated in how many professional contests prior to his meeting with Henry Cooper?**
(a) 52 (b) 53 (c) 54

**50. On 20 October 1959, British featherweight champion Bobby Neill was stopped in which round by Davey Moore?**
(a) One (b) Two (c) Three

**51. At the time of the contest with Bobby Neill, Davey Moore was a reigning world champion in which weight division?**
(a) Bantamweight (b) Featherweight (c) super-featherweight

**52. In a contest set for ten rounds, Nino Valdes defeated opponent Brian London on 1 December 1959 by which method?**
(a) Six-round knockout (b) Seven-round retirement (c) Nine-round knockout

**53. Who was the referee of the Valdes-London contest?**
(a) Ike Powell (b) Jack Hart (c) Bill Williams

**54. What was the nationality of Nino Valdes?**
(a) Cuban (b) Spanish (c) Mexican

**55. On 16 April 1960, Pone Kingpetch won the world flyweight title when he defeated holder Pascual Perez by which method?**
(a) Four-round stoppage (b) Nine-round knockout (c) 15-round points decision.

**56. In which country did the Kingpetch-Perez title contest take place?**
(a) Argentina (b) Japan (c) Thailand

**57. At this stage of his career Pascual Perez had now participated in how many professional contests?**
(a) 57 (b) 58 (c) 59

**58. Who was the referee of the Kingpetch-Perez title contest?**
(a) Chuer Chaksuraksa (b) Lorenzo Torreoalba (c) Mushy Callahan.

**59. At the time of the Kingpetch-Perez title contest, who was the reigning world featherweight champion?**
(a) Vicente Saldivar (b) Davey Moore (c) Sugar Ramos

60. *Salvatore Burruni won the European flyweight title on 29 June 1961 when he outpointed holder Risto Luukkonen over 15 rounds. How many years of age was Burruni when he won the championship?*
(a) 27 (b) 28 (c) 29

61. *How many professional contests had Salvatore Burruni participated in prior to winning the European title?*
(a) 31 (b) 32 (c) 33

62. *Before being stopped in round four on 10 February 1962, Sonny Banks became the first man to floor Muhammad Ali for a count in the professional ranks. In which round did Banks score the respective knockdown?*
(a) One (b) Two (c) Three

63. *Rocky Gattellari won the Australian flyweight crown on 26 February 1962 when he knocked out defending champion Jackie Bruce in which round?*
(a) Six (b) Seven (c) Eight

64. *Who was the referee of the Gattellari-Bruce title contest?*
(a) Vic Patrick (b) Les Pearson (c) Ronnie James

65. *Howard Winstone successfully defended his British featherweight crown on 10 April 1962 when he stopped challenger Derry Treanor in which round?*
(a) 12 (b) 13 (c) 14

66. *Who was the referee of the Winstone-Treanor title contest?*
(a) Jack Hart (b) Wally Thom (c) Harry Gibbs

67. *Where in the UK was the venue for the Winstone-Treanor title contest?*
(a) Sophia Gardens Pavilion, Cardiff (b) Empire Pool, Wembley, London (c) Maindy Stadium, Cardiff

68. *Eddie Thomas was the manager of Howard Winstone. When boxing in the professional ranks, Thomas was a British, European and Commonwealth champion in which weight division?*
(a) Welterweight (b) Middleweight (c) Light-heavyweight

69. *Olli Maki became the first holder of the European super-lightweight title on 14 February 1964 when he defeated opponent Conny Rudhof by way of a 15-round points decision. In which country did the contest take place?*
(a) Norway (b) Finland (c) Germany

70. *Conny Rudhof had previously held a European title in which other weight division?*
(a) Bantamweight (b) Featherweight (c) Lightweight

**71. Karl Mildenberger won the vacant European heavyweight crown on 17 October 1964 when he knocked out opponent Santo Amonti in which round?**

(a) One (b) Two (c) Three

**72. Who held the European title prior to Karl Mildenberger?**

(a) Ingemar Johansson (b) Henry Cooper (c) Dick Richardson

**73. Alan Rudkin defeated opponent Mimoun Ben Ali on 27 April 1965, outpointing him over how many rounds?**

(a) Six (b) Eight (c) Ten

**74. At the time of his contest with Alan Rudkin, Mimoun Ben Ali was a reigning European champion in which weight division?**

(a) Flyweight (b) Bantamweight (c) Featherweight

**75. On 24 May 1965 Memo Ayon won a ten-round points decision over which opponent?**

(a) Carl Bobo Olson (b) Sugar Ray Robinson (c) Joey Giardello

**76. Billy Walker and Eduardo Corletti met in a ten-round contest on 19 August 1965, but what was the result?**

(a) A draw (b) Points win for Walker (c) Points win for Corletti

**77. In which country did the Walker-Corletti contest take place?**

(a) England (b) Italy (c) Argentina

**78. What was the nationality of Eduardo Corletti?**

(a) Argentine (b) Italian (c) German

**79. On 1 April 1966 Johnny Famechon retained his Australian featherweight title when he defeated challenger Domenico Chiloiro by which method?**

(a) Six-round stoppage (b) Ten-round knockout (c) 15-round points decision

**80. On 6 September 1966 Walter McGowan won the British and Commonwealth bantamweight titles when he defeated holder Alan Rudkin by which method?**

(a) Six-round stoppage (b) Eight-round knockout (c) 15-round point's decision

**81. Who was the referee of the McGowan-Rudkin title contest?**

(a) Harry Gibbs (b) Billy Jones (c) Ike Powell

**82. Before the Alan Rudkin contest, Walter McGowan had participated in how many professional contests?**

(a) 26 (b) 27 (c) 28

**83. In his last professional contest, which took place on 12 September 1966, Brian Curvis stopped opponent Des Rea in which round?**

(a) Six (b) Seven (c) Eight

**84. During his career, Brian Curvis participated in how many professional contests?**
(a) 40 (b) 41 (c) 42

**85. Which title in the welterweight division did Brian Curvis fail to win during his time in the professional ranks?**
(a) British (b) Commonwealth (c) European

**86. In which part of the UK was Brian Curvis born?**
(a) England (b) Wales (c) Scotland

**87. After his defeat to Brian Curvis, Des Rea continued his career and eventually won a British title in which weight division?**
(a) Lightweight (b) Super-lightweight (c) Welterweight

**88. Muhammad Ali retained his world heavyweight title on 22 March 1967 when he knocked out challenger Zora Folley in which round?**
(a) Six (b) Seven (c) Eight

**89. Who was the referee of the Ali-Folley title contest?**
(a) Johnny LoBianco (b) Jackie Silvers (c) Harry Kessler

**90. At this stage of his career Muhammad Ali was now undefeated in how many professional contests?**
(a) 27 (b) 29 (c) 30

**91. Zora Folley had participated in how many professional contests before facing Muhammad Ali for the world heavyweight crown?**
(a) 84 (b) 85 (c) 86

**92. On 11 May 1967 Ken Buchanan stopped opponent Franco Brondi in which round?**
(a) Three (b) Four (c) Five

**93. Prior to facing Ken Buchanan, Franco Brondi was a former European champion in which weight division?**
(a) Featherweight (b) Lightweight (c) Welterweight

**94. Takeshi Fuji successfully defended his undisputed world super-lightweight title when he knocked out challenger Willi Quatuor in which round on 16 November 1967?**
(a) Two (b) Three (c) Four

**95. Who was the referee of the Fuji-Quatuor title contest?**
(a) Lee Grossman (b) Jay Edson (c) Dick Young

**96. What was the nationality of Willi Quatuor?**

(a) Swedish (b) German (c) Austrian

**97. Johnny Pritchett outpointed opponent Wilbert McClure over how many rounds on 5 December 1967?**

(a) Eight (b) Nine (c) Ten

**98. Who was the referee of the Pritchett-McClure contest?**

(a) Harry Gibbs (b) Wally Thom (c) Bill White

**99. Where was the venue in the UK for the Pritchett-McClure contest?**

(a) King's Hall, Belle Vue Manchester, Lancashire (b) Ice Rink, Nottingham, Nottinghamshire (c) Royal Albert Hall, Kensington, London

**100. At the 1960 Olympic Games, which took place in Rome, Italy Wilbert McClure won a gold medal in which weight division?**

(a) Welterweight (b) Light-Middleweight (c) Middleweight

**101. Hiroshi Kobayashi captured the WBA and WBC world super-featherweight crown on 14 December 1967 when he knocked out defending champion Yoshiaki Numata in round 12. In which country did this contest take place?**

(a) Mexico (b) Japan (c) Thailand

**102. Jimmy Anderson became the first holder of the British super-featherweight title on 20 February 1968 when he stopped opponent Jimmy Revie in which round?**

(a) Seven (b) Eight (c) Nine

**103. Who was the referee of the Anderson-Revie title contest?**

(a) Wally Thom (b) Bill Williams (c) Harry Gibbs

**104. Going into the contest against Jimmy Anderson, Jimmy Revie was undefeated in how many professional contests?**

(a) 11 (b) 12 (c) 13

**105. At the time of the Anderson-Revie title contest, who was the reigning world lightweight champion?**

(a) Carlos Ortiz (b) Carlos Teo Cruz (c) Mando Ramos

**106. On 12 November 1968, Billy Walker defeated Thad Spencer when he stopped him in which round?**

(a) Five (b) Six (c) Seven

**107. Who was the referee of the Walker-Spencer contest?**

(a) Roland Dakin (b) Harry Gibbs (c) Bill Williams

**108. Where in the UK was the venue for the Walker-Spencer contest?**

(a) Royal Albert Hall, Kensington, London (b) Empire Pool, Wembley London (c) Olympia, Kensington, London

**109. Jimmy Revie won the vacant British featherweight title on 24 March 1969 when opponent John O'Brien retired in which round?**

(a) Five (b) Six (c) Seven

**110. Who was the referee of the Revie-O'Brien title contest?**

(a) Harry Gibbs (b) Wally Thom (c) Sid Nathan

**111. Who held the British featherweight title prior to Jimmy Revie?**

(a) Terry Spinks (b) Bobby Neill (c) Howard Winstone

**112. Jack Bodell made history when he became the first boxer with the southpaw stance to win the British heavyweight championship in a contest that took place on 13 October 1969. Bodell duly defeated opponent Carl Gizzi for the vacant crown by which method?**

(a) Two-round stoppage (b) Eight-round knockout (c) 15-round points decision

**113. John McCluskey outpointed Fritz Chervet over ten rounds on 26 December 1969. Where in Switzerland did the contest take place?**

(a)  Frauenfeld (b) Zurich (c) Berne

**114. During the course of his career, Fritz Chervet went on to win a European title in which weight division?**

(a) Flyweight (b) Bantamweight (c) Featherweight

**115. On 12 May 1970 Joe Bugner stopped opponent Brian London in which round?**

(a) Four (b) Five (c) Six

**116. At this stage of his career, Joe Bugner had now participated in how many professional contests?**

(a) 28 (b) 29 (c) 30

**117. At this stage of his career, Brian London had now participated in how many professional contests?**

(a) 56 (b) 57 (c) 58

**118. During his professional career, which title in the heavyweight division did Brian London not hold?**

a) British (b) Commonwealth (c) European

**119. At the time of the Bugner-London contest, who was the reigning world heavyweight champion?**

(a) Joe Frazier (b) George Foreman (c) Muhammad Ali

**120. On 4 June 1970, Emile Griffith met Tom Bogs in a ten-round contest, but what was the result?**

(a) A six-round knock victory for Bogs (b) A draw (c) Points win for Griffith

**121. Who was the referee of the Griffith-Bogs contest?**

(a) Julian Risoto (b) Harry Gibbs (c) Ejner Roth

**122. In which country did the Griffith-Bogs contest take place?**

(a) Denmark (b) Finland (c) Austria

**123. At the time of his contest with Griffith, Bogs was a European champion in which weight division?**

(a) Welterweight (b) Middleweight (c) Light-heavyweight

**124. On 24 January 1971 Chris Finnegan became the new British and Commonwealth light-heavyweight champion when he stopped defending title holder Eddie Avoth in which round?**

(a) 13 (b) 14 (c) 15

**125. Henry Cooper lost his British, European and Commonwealth heavyweight titles on 16 March 1971 to challenger Joe Bugner when defeated by which method?**

(a) Six-round stoppage (b) Nine-round knockout (c) 15-round points decision

**126. Who was the referee of the Cooper-Bugner title contest?**

(a) Harry Gibbs (b) Roland Dakin (c) James Brimmell

**127. At this stage of his career Henry Cooper had now participated in how many professional contests?**

(a) 54 (b) 55 (c) 56

**128. At this stage of his career, Joe Bugner had now participated in how many professional contests?**

(a) 35 (b) 36 (c) 37

**129. At the time of the Joe Bugner contest, how many years of age was Henry Cooper?**

(a) 35 (b) 36 (c) 37

**130. At the time of the Henry Cooper contest, how many years of age was Joe Bugner?**

(a) 21 (b) 22 (c) 23

**131. During his professional career, on how many separate occasions did Henry Cooper win the British heavyweight title?**

(a) Once (b) Twice (c) Three times

**132. How many Lonsdale belts did Henry Cooper win outright for British heavyweight championship victories during his title reign?**
(a) One (b) Two (c) Three

**133. During his professional career, on how many separate occasions did Henry Cooper win the European heavyweight title?**
(a) Once (b) Twice (c) Three times

**134. In which year did Henry Cooper become the first boxer to receive a Knighthood?**
(a) 2000 (b) 2001 (c) 2002

**135. Ken Buchanan stopped opponent Carlos Hernandez in which round on 11 May 1971?**
(a) Seven (b) Eight (c) Nine

**136. Carlos Hernandez was a former world champion in which weight division?**
(a) Featherweight (b) Lightweight (c) Super-lightweight

**137. What was the nationality of Carlos Hernandez?**
(a) Venezuelan (b) Mexican (c) American

**138. In defence of his Commonwealth welterweight crown on 5 September 1971, Ralph Charles stopped challenger Jeff White in which round?**
(a) Four (b) Five (c) Six

**139. In which country did the Charles-White title contest take place?**
(a) England (b) New Zealand (c) Australia

**140. On 9 May 1972 Jerry Quarry met Larry Middleton in a ten-round contest. What was the result?**
(a) Points win for Quarry (b) Points win for Middleton (c) A draw

**141. In which country did the Quarry-Middleton contest take place?**
(a) America (b) Canada (c) England

**142. Enrique Pinder won the world bantamweight crown on 29 July 1972 when he defeated defending champion Rafael Herrera by which method?**
(a) Six-round stoppage (b) Nine-round knockout (c) 15-round points decision.

**143. Jerry Quarry and Earnie Shavers met in a contest scheduled for ten rounds on 14 December 1973. What was the result?**
(a) Quarry won by a one-round stoppage. (b) Shavers won by a six-round knockout
(c) Contest declared a draw

**144. Who was the referee of the Quarry-Shavers contest?**
(a) Davey Pearl (b) Arthur Mercante (c) Buddy Basilico

**145. Kevin Finnegan won the British middleweight championship on 11 February 1974 when he defeated defending title holder Bunny Sterling by which method?**
(a) Four-round retirement (b) Six-round stoppage (c) 15-round points decision

**146. The Commonwealth flyweight title changed hands on 13 March 1974 when challenger Big Jim West stopped defending champion Henry Nissen in which round?**
(a) Three (b) Four (c) Five

**147. Who was the referee of the West-Nissen title contest?**
(a) Vic Patrick (b) Ken Brady (c) Terry Reilly

**148. Where in Australia was the venue for the West-Nissen title contest?**
(a) Festival Hall Melbourne, Victoria (b) St Kilda Town Hall, Melbourne, Victoria (c) Iceland Arena, Melbourne, Victoria

**149. Johnny Clark had his last professional contest on 16 May 1974 when he defeated opponent Luigi Tessarin by which method?**
(a) Three-round stoppage (b) Six-round knockout (c) Ten-round points decision

**150. How many contests had Johnny Clark participated in during his professional career?**
(a) 43 (b) 44 (c) 45

**151. Which title in the bantamweight division did Johnny Clark fail to win during his time in the professional ranks?**
(a) British (b) Commonwealth (c) European

**152. John H. Stracey won the European welterweight title on 27 May 1974 when he stopped defending champion Roger Menetrey in round eight. In which country did this contest take place?**
(a) England (b) France (c) Switzerland

**153. Before losing his title to John H. Stracey, how many successful defences of the European championship had Roger Menetrey made?**
(a) Five (b) Six (c) Seven

**154. On 24 March 1975 Muhammad Ali successfully defended his world heavyweight title against challenger Chuck Wepner, stopping him in which round?**
(a) 13 (b) 14 (c) 15

**155. In which round was Muhammad Ali floored for a count by Chuck Wepner during the title contest?**
(a) Eight (b) Nine (c) Ten

**156. Who was the referee of the Ali-Wepner title contest?**
(a) Tony Perez (b) Fred Hernandez (c) Zach Clayton

**157. Where in the USA was the venue for the Ali-Wepner title contest?**
(a) Astrodome, Houston, Texas (b) Madison Square Garden, New York (c) Richfield Coliseum, Richfield, Ohio

**158. What was Chuck Wepner's nickname?**
(a) Bayonne Warrior (b) Bayonne Bleeder (c) Bayonne Enforcer

**159 At this stage of his career, Chuck Wepner had now participated in how many professional contests?**
(a) 41 (b) 42 (c) 43

**160. At this stage of his career, Muhammad Ali had now participated in how many professional contests?**
(a) 47 (b) 48 (c) 49

**161. How many world heavyweight title contests had Muhammad Ali now participated in?**
(a) 13 (b) 14 (c) 15

**162. Jim Watt retained his European lightweight title on 17 February 1978 when he outpointed challenger Perico Fernandez over 15 rounds. In which country did the contest take place?**
(a) Spain (b) England (c) Italy

**163. Perico Fernandez was a former WBC world champion in which weight division?**
(a) Featherweight (b) Lightweight (c) Super-lightweight

**164. On 15 September 1978, Jorge Lujan retained his WBA world bantamweight crown when he defeated challenger Alberto Davila by which method?**
(a) Five-round disqualification (b) Six-round knockout (c) 15-round points decision

**165. Who was the reigning WBA world flyweight champion at the time of the Lujan-Davila world title contest?**
(a) Betulio Gonzalez (b) Luis Ibarra (c) Tae Shik Kim

**166. The vacant WBC world lightweight championship was filled on 17 April 1979 when Jim Watt stepped into the ring with Alfredo Pitalua and won the crown with a stoppage in which round?**
(a) Ten (b) 11 (c) 12

**167. Who was the referee of the Watt-Pitalua title contest?**
(a) Carlos Padilla (b) Arthur Mercante (c) Sid Nathan

*168. At this stage of his career, how many professional contests had Jim Watt now participated in?*
(a) 39 (b) 40 (c) 41

*169. Maurice Hope celebrated a night of triumph when he successfully defended his WBC world super-welterweight crown on 26 November 1980, defeating challenger Carlos Herrera by which method?*
(a) Three-round stoppage (b) Nine-round knockout (c) 15-round points decision.

*170. In which country did the Hope-Herrera title contest take place?*
(a) England (b) Argentina (c) Italy

*171. On 1 October 1985, Frank Bruno took over as European heavyweight champion when he knocked out defending title holder Anders Eklund in which round?*
(a) Three (b) Four (c) Five

*172. Who was the last British boxer to hold the European crown prior to Bruno?*
(a) Joe Bugner (b) John L. Gardner (c) Richard Dunn

*173. Terry Marsh won the vacant European super-lightweight title on 24 October 1985 when he knocked out opponent Alessandro Scapecchi in which round?*
(a) Five (b) Six (c) Seven

*174. Which boxer held the European title prior to Terry Marsh?*
(a) Patrizio Oliva (b) Robert Gambini (c) Clinton McKenzie

*175. Mike Tyson stopped opponent Jesse Ferguson in which round on 16 February 1986?*
(a) Five (b) Six (c) Seven

*176. At this stage of his career, Mike Tyson was now undefeated in how many professional contests?*
(a) 18 (b) 19 (c) 20

*177. At the time of the Tyson-Ferguson contest, who was the reigning WBA world heavyweight champion?*
(a) Greg Page (b) Tim Witherspoon (c) Tony Tubbs

*178. On 25 April 1990, Chris Eubank made a successful defence of his WBC International middleweight title defeating challenger Eduardo Domingo Contreras by which method?*
(a) Five-round stoppage (b) Nine-round stoppage (c) 12-round points decision

*179. At this stage of his career, Chris Eubank was now undefeated in how many professional contests?*
(a) 21 (b) 22 (c) 23

*180. How many contests did Chris Eubank participate in during the course of 1990?*
(a) Four (b) Five (c) Six

*181. Gary De'Roux captured the British featherweight title on 5 March 1991 when he knocked out holder Sean Murphy in which round?*
(a) Four (b) Five (c) Six

*182. Where in the UK was the venue for the De'Roux-Murphy contest?*
(a) Sports Centre, Lord Street, Oldham, Lancashire (b) York Hall, Bethnal Green, London (c) London Arena, Millwall, London

*183. How many professional bouts had Gary De'Roux participated in prior to meeting Sean Murphy?*
(a) 17 (b) 18 (c) 19

*184. How many professional bouts had Sean Murphy participated in prior to meeting Gary De'Roux*
(a) 20 (b) 21 (c) 22

*185. Duke McKenzie became a three-weight world champion when he won the WBO world super-bantamweight title, outpointing defending champion Jesse Benavides over 12 rounds on the 15 October 1992. Prior to this contest, which world crown did McKenzie not hold?*
(a) IBF flyweight (b) WBC Super-flyweight (c) WBO bantamweight

*186. Jerry Quarry met opponent Ron Cranmer on 30 October 1992 in his last professional contest. How many rounds was the bout scheduled for?*
(a) Six (B) Eight (c) Ten

*187. What was the result of the Quarry-Cranmer contest?*
(a) Points win for Quarry (b) Points win for Cranmer (c) A draw

*188. How many professional bouts had Jerry Quarry participated in during his career?*
(a) 66 (B) 67 (C) 68

*189. During his career in the professional ranks, which British boxer did Jerry Quarry not meet?*
(a) Brian London (b) Jack Bodell (c) Billy Walker

*190. For the first time in the history of boxing, two British fighters contested a version of the world heavyweight title on 1 October 1993. Title holder Lennox Lewis duly stepped into the ring and successfully defended his WBC world heavyweight crown, stopping challenger Frank Bruno in which round?*
(a) Seven (b) Eight (c) Nine

**191. Who was the referee of the Lewis-Bruno title contest?**
(a) Joe Cortez (b) Mickey Vann (c) Frank Cappuccino

**192. Where in the UK was the venue for the Lewis-Bruno title contest?**
(a) Earls Court Exhibition Hall, Kensington, London (b) Wembley Arena, Wembley, London (c) National Stadium, Cardiff, Wales

**193. At this stage of his professional career, Lennox Lewis was now undefeated in how many contests?**
(a) 23 (b) 24 (c)25

**194. On 12 October 1994 Johnny Tapia stopped opponent Henry Martinez in which round to capture the vacant WBO world super-flyweight crown?**
(a) 10 (b) 11 (c) 12

**195. On 2 September 1995 Frank Bruno boxed his way to the world heavyweight crown when he outpointed defending champion Oliver McCall over 12 rounds. Which version of the title did Bruno win on this occasion?**
(a) WBC (b) IBF (c) WBA

**196. Oscar De La Hoya won the WBC world super-lightweight title on 7 June 1996 when he stopped holder Julio Cesar Chavez in which round?**
(a) Three (b) Four (c) Five

**197. At the time of his title challenge to Julio Cesar Chavez, Oscar De La Hoya was undefeated in how many professional contests?**
(a) 19 (b) 20 (c) 21

**198. Who was the referee of the De La Hoya-Chavez title contest?**
(a) Joe Cortez (b) Ron Lipton (c) Laurence Cole

**199. Where in the USA was the venue for the De La-Hoya-Chavez title contest?**
(a) Thomas & Mack Center, Las Vegas, Nevada (b) Staples Center, Los Angeles, California (c) Caesars Palace, Las Vegas, Nevada

**200. Henry Akinwande won the vacant WBO world heavyweight title on 29 June 1996 when he knocked out Jeremy Williams in which round?**
(a) Three (b) Four (c) Five

**201. Who was the referee of the Akinwande-Williams title contest?**
(a) Mills Lane (b) Raul Caiz Sr (c) Richard Steele

**202. Who held the WBO world heavyweight title prior to Henry Akinwande?**
(a) Herbie Hide (b) Riddick Bowe (c) Michael Bentt

**203. What was Henry Akinwande's listed height?**

(a) 6ft 7in (b) 6ft 8in (c) 6ft 9in

**204. Which of the following titles had Henry Akinwande not held prior to his stepping into the ring to fight Jeremy Williams for the WBO world heavyweight crown?**

(a) European (b) Commonwealth (c) British

**205. On 26 August 1996 Yuri Arbachakov retained his WBC world flyweight title when he stopped challenger Puma Toguchi in which round?**

(a) Seven (b) Eight (c) Nine

**206. How many successful defences of the WBC world flyweight title had Yuri Arbachakov now made?**

(a) Nine (b) Ten (c) 11

**207. In which country did the Arbachakov-Toguchi title contest take place?**

(a) Mexico (b) Japan (c) England

**208. Who was the reigning IBF world flyweight title holder at the time of the Arbachakov-Toguchi contest?**

(a) Francisco Tejedor (b) Danny Romero jr (c) Mark Johnson

**209. George Foreman retained his WBU world heavyweight title and won the vacant IBA version of the crown on 3 November 1996 when he defeated opponent Crawford Grimsley by which method?**

(a) Three-round knockout (b) Eight-round stoppage (c) 12-round points decision

**210. In which country did the Foreman-Grimsley title contest take place?**

(a) Japan (b) America (c) Argentina

**211. On 2 March 1997 Jane Couch successfully defended her WIBF world super-lightweight title stopping challenger Andrea DeShong in which round?**

(a) Five (b) Six (c) Seven

**212. In which country did the Couch-DeShong title contest take place?**

(a) America (b) England (c) Canada

**213. What was Jane Couch's nickname?**

(a) Nightmare Assassin (b) Fleetwood Assassin (c) Sleepless Assassin

**214. Lennox Lewis made short work of his challenger Andrew Golota on 4 October 1997 when defending his WBC world heavyweight crown, retaining his title in sensational style by way of a knockout in the first round. How many bouts had Lewis now won in the first round during his professional career?**

(a) Three (b) Four (c) Five

**215. Who was the referee of the Lewis-Golota title contest?**

(a) Joe Cortez (b) Mitch Halpern (c) Frank Cappuccino

**216. Manny Pacquiao won the WBC world flyweight title on 4 December 1998 when he knocked out defending champion Chatchai Sasakul in which round?**

(a) Seven (b) Eight (c) Nine

**217. Who was the referee of the Pacquiao-Sasakul title contest?**

(a) Richard Steele (b) Malcolm Bulner (c) Carlos Padilla

**218. In which country did the Pacquiao-Sasakul title contest take place?**

(a) Thailand (b) Philippines (c) Australia

**219. At the time of the Pacquiao-Sasakul title contest, who was the reigning WBA world flyweight champion?**

(a) Jose Bonilla (b) Hugo Rafael Soto (c) Leo Gamez

**220. Paul Ingle retained his IBF world featherweight title and also won the IBO featherweight crown from Junior Jones on 29 April 2000 when winning by a stoppage in which round?**

(a) 10 (b) 11 (c) 12

**221. In which country did the Ingle-Jones title contest take place?**

(a) America (b) Canada (c) England

**222. What was Paul Ingle's nickname?**

(a) Yorkshire Destroyer (b) Yorkshire Terminator (c) Yorkshire Hunter

**223. Jane Couch defeated opponent Carla Witherspoon, outpointing her over how many rounds on 28 July 2001?**

(a) Four (b) Six (c) Eight

**224. In which country did the Couch-Witherspoon contest take place?**

(a) America (b) Jamaica (c) England

**225. Vitali Klitschko became the new WBC world heavyweight champion on 24 April 2004 when he stopped Corrie Sanders in which round to win the vacant crown?**

(a) Eight (b) Nine (c) Ten

**226. Where in the USA was the venue for the Klitschko-Sanders title contest?**

(a) Hilton Hotel, Las Vegas, Nevada (b) Staples Center, Los Angeles, California (c) Madison Square Garden, New York

*227. On 16 April 2005 Hozumi Hasegawa won the WBC world bantamweight title when he outpointed holder Veeraphol Sahaprom over 12 rounds. How many successful defences of the championship had Sahaprom made before losing his crown?*

(a) 12 (b) 13 (c) 14

*228. Nikolai Valuev won the WBA world heavyweight crown on 17 December 2005, defeating defending title holder John Ruiz by which method?*

(a) Five-round disqualification (b) Seven-round knockout (c) 12-round points decision

*229. At that time Nikolai Valuev made boxing history as he became the tallest man to hold a version of the world heavyweight championship. What was his listed height?*

(a) 6ft 5in (b) 6ft 8in (c) 7ft

*230. In which country did the Valuev-Ruiz title contest take place?*

(a) Russia (b) Germany (c) France

*231. What was the nationality of Valuev?*

(a) Russian (b) Polish (c) German

*232. Muhammad Rachman retained his IBF world minimumweight title on 6 May 2006 when he knocked out challenger Omar Soto in which round?*

(a) Four (b) Five (c) Six

*233. Who was the referee of the Rachman-Soto title contest?*

(a) Wayne Hedgpeth (b) John Wright (c) Bruce McTavish

*234. In which country did the Rachman-Soto title contest take place?*

(a) Indonesia (b) Australia (c) Japan

*235. On 14 October 2006 Joe Calzaghe retained his WBO and IBF world super-middleweight titles when he outpointed challenger Sakio Bika over 12 rounds. At this stage of his career Calzaghe was now undefeated in how many professional contests?*

(a) 41 (b) 42 (c) 43

*236. Laila Ali retained her world female WBC and WIBA super-middleweight titles on 3 February 2007 when she stopped challenger Gwendolyn O'Neil in which round?*

(a) One (b) Two (c) Three

*237. In which country did the Ali-O'Neil title contest take place?*

(a) America (b) Canada (c) South Africa

**238. At this stage of her career Laila Ali was now undefeated in how many professional contests?**
(a) 23 (b) 24 (c) 25

**239. Kell Brook became the new British welterweight champion on 14 June 2008 when he stopped opponent Barrie Jones in which round to win the vacant crown?**
(a) Seven (b) Nine (c) Ten

**240. Who held the British welterweight title prior to Kell Brook?**
(a) Kevin Anderson (b) Kevin McIntyre (c) Young Mutley

**241. Who was the referee of the Brook-Jones title contest?**
(a) Dave Parris (b) Victor Loughlin (c) Mickey Vann

**242. At this stage of his career Kell Brook was now undefeated in how many professional contests?**
(a) 16 (b) 17 (c) 18

**243. Moruti Mthalane won the vacant IBF world flyweight championship on 20 November 2009 when he outpointed opponent Julio Cesar Miranda over 12 rounds. Who was the previous holder of this title?**
(a) Vic Darchinyan (b) Nonito Donaire (c) Irene Pacheco

**244. Tyson Fury emerged victorious in his contest on 18 December 2010 when he defeated opponent Zack Page by way of a points decision over how many rounds?**
(a) Six (b) Eight (c) Nine

**245. In which country did the Fury-Page contest take place?**
(a) Australia (b) England (c) Canada

**246. At this stage of his career Tyson Fury was now undefeated in how many professional contests?**
(a) 11 (b) 12 (c) 13

**247. Matthew Hatton failed to win the vacant WBC world super-welterweight title on 5 March 2011 when Saul Alvarez defeated him by which method?**
(a) Six-round stoppage (b) Nine-round retirement (c) 12-round points decision.

**248. In which weight division had Matthew Hatton previously held a European title?**
(a) Welterweight (b) Super-welterweight (c) Middleweight

**249. James DeGale made a successful defence of his European super-middleweight title on 21 April 2012 when he stopped challenger Cristian Sanavia in which round?**
(a) Four (b) Five (c) Six

**250. In which country did the DeGale-Sanavia title contest take place?**
(a) Denmark (b) Norway (c) Italy

**251. What was the nationality of Cristian Sanavia?**
(a) Danish (b) Italian (c) Norwegian

**252. Which version of the world super-middleweight title did Cristian Sanavia formerly hold?**
(a) WBC (b) WBA (c) IBF

**253. On 16 February 2013 Adrien Broner stepped into the ring as the reigning WBC world lightweight champion and left the battle ground still wearing the crown when challenger Gavin Rees was stopped in which round?**
(a) Three (b) Four (c) Five

**254. What was Adrien Broner's nickname?**
(a) The Problem (b) The Mystery (c) The Puzzle

**255. Adrien Broner, prior to his contest with Gavin Rees, was a former holder of which other world title?**
(a) WBA super-bantamweight (b) WBC featherweight (c) WBO super-featherweight

**256. Gavin Rees, prior to his contest with Adrien Broner, was a former holder of which other world title?**
(a) WBC Super-bantamweight (b) WBO featherweight (c) WBA Super-lightweight

**257. On 20 April 2013 Tyson Fury made his American debut knocking out opponent Steve Cunningham in which round?**
(a) Seven (b) Eight (c) Nine

**258. In which round did Steve Cunningham floor Tyson Fury for a count during the contest?**
(a) One (b) Two (c) Three

**259. Steve Cunningham had by then participated in how many professional contests?**
(a) 30 (b) 31 (c) 32

**260. Lucas Browne won the vacant WBF world heavyweight title on 28 April 2013 when he outpointed opponent James Toney over 12 rounds. In which country did the contest take place?**
(a) America (b) Australia (c) Canada

**261. At this stage of his career, Lucas Browne was now undefeated in how many professional contests?**
(a) 16 (b) 17 (c) 18

262. Floyd Mayweather Jr. outpointed defending champion Saul Alvarez over 12 rounds on 14 September 2013 to win the WBA super world super-welterweight crown and WBC world super-welterweight title. Two of the three ringside judges were Craig Metcalfe and Dave Moretti. Who was the third official?
(a) Julie Lederman (b) CJ Ross (c) Jerry Roth

263. Dereck Chisora became the new European heavyweight champion on 21 September 2013 when he stopped his opponent Edmund Gerber in which round to win the vacant title?
(a) Four (b) Five (c) Six

264. Who was the last British boxer prior to Dereck Chisora to hold the European heavyweight title?
(a) Henry Akinwande (b) Matt Skelton (c) Audley Harrison

265. Demetrius Andrade won the vacant WBO world super-welterweight title on 9 November 2013 when he defeated opponent Vanes Martirosyan by which method?
(a) Six-round stoppage (b) Nine-round knockout (c) 12-round points decision

266. On 9 November 2013 Oleksandr Usyk made his professional debut stopping opponent Felipe Romero in which round?
(a) Four (b) Five (c) Six

267. In which country did the Usyk-Romero contest take place?
(a) Ukraine (b) Germany (c) Poland

268. At the London 2012 Olympic game's Oleksandr Usyk won a gold medal in which weight division?
(a) Middleweight (b) Light-heavyweight (c) Heavyweight

269. Naoya Inoue won the WBC world light-flyweight crown on 6 April 2014 when he knocked out defending title holder Adrian Hernandez in which round?
(a) Six (b) Seven (c) Eight

270. In which country did the Inoue-Hernandez title contest take place?
(a) Mexico (b) Japan (c) Australia

271. Who was the referee of the Inoue-Hernandez title contest?
(a) Lou Moret (b) Mark Nelson (c) Michael Griffin

272. At this stage of his career Naoya Inoue was now undefeated in how many professional contests?
(a) Six (b) Seven (c) Eight

**273. Vasiliy Lomachenko won the vacant WBO world featherweight title on 21 June 2014 when he defeated opponent Gary Russell Jr by which method?**
(a) Six-round stoppage (b) Nine-round knockout (c) 12-round points decision

**274. At this stage of his career Vasiliy Lomachenko had now participated in how professional many contests?**
(a) One (b) Two (c) Three

**275. At this stage of his career Gary Russell Jr had now participated in how many professional contests?**
(a) 24 (b) 25 (c) 26

**276. Guillermo Rigondeaux successfully retained his WBA super world super-bantamweight and WBO world super-bantamweight titles on 19 July 2014 when he knocked out challenger Anusorn Yotjan in which round?**
(a) One (b) Two (c) Three

**277. In which country did the Rigondeaux-Yotjan title contest take place?**
(a) Thailand (b) China (c) Japan

**278. What is the nationality of Guillermo Rigondeaux?**
(a) Mexican (b) Spanish (c) Cuban

**279. Billy Joe Saunders won the vacant European middleweight title on 26 July 2014 when he knocked out opponent Emanuele Blandamura in which round?**
(a) Eight (b) Nine (c) Ten

**280. Going into the contest against Emanuele Blandamura, Billy Joe Saunders was undefeated in how many professional contests?**
(a) 17 (b) 18 (c) 19

**281. Going into the contest with Billy Joe Saunders, Emanuele Blandamura was undefeated in how many professional contests?**
(a) 21 (b) 22 (c) 23

**282. Who held the European middleweight title prior to Billy Joe Saunders?**
(a) Grzegorz Proksa (b) Kerry Hope (c) Maksym Bursak

**283. What was the nationality of Emanuele Blandamura?**
(a) Italian (b) Spanish (c) German

**284. Cecilia Braekhus had a successful outing on 29 November 2014 when she retained her WBC WBA IBF and WBO female world welterweight titles defeating challenger Jennifer Retzke by which method?**
(a) Four-round stoppage (b) Six-round knockout (c) Ten-round points decision

**285. Who was the referee of the Braekhus-Retzke title contest?**

(a) Sparkle Lee (b) Phil Edwards (c) Stefano Carozza

**286. At this stage of her career Cecilia Braekhus was now undefeated in how many professional contests?**

(a) 26 (b) 27 (c) 28

**287. On 13 December 2014 Andy Lee won the vacant WBO world middleweight title when he stopped opponent Matvey Korobov in which round?**

(a) Six (b) Seven (c) Eight

**288. Going into the contest against Andy Lee, Matvey Korobov was undefeated in how many professional contests?**

(a) 23 (b) 24 (c) 25

**289. Going into the contest against Andy Lee, Matvey Korobov had previously won how many of his bouts inside the scheduled distance?**

(a) 13 (b) 14 (c) 15

**290. James DeGale won the vacant IBF world super-middleweight title on 23 May 2015 when he outpointed opponent Andre Dirrell over 12 rounds. In which country did this contest take place?**

(a) England (b) Canada (c) America

**291. Who was the previous holder of the IBF world title prior to James DeGale?**

(a) Carl Froch (b) Lucian Bute (c) Alejandro Berrio

**292. On 18 July 2015 Scott Quigg made a successful defence of his WBA world super-bantamweight crown when he stopped Kiko Martinez in two rounds. Which version of the world title did Martinez previously hold?**

(a) WBC (b) IBF (c) WBO

**293. What was the nationality of Kiko Martinez?**

(a) Spanish (b) Italian (c) Mexican

**294. Errol Spence Jr defeated opponent Chris Van Heerden on 11 September 2015, stopping him in which round?**

(a) Six (b) Seven (c) Eight

**295. At this stage of his career Errol Spence Jr was now undefeated in how many professional contests?**

(a) 17 (b) 18 (c) 19

**296. In which country did the Spence Jr-Van Heerden contest take place?**

(a) Canada (b) America (c) Mexico

**297. Anthony Joshua defended his WBC International heavyweight crown and won the vacant Commonwealth heavyweight title on 12 September 2015 when he stopped opponent Gary Cornish in which round?**
(a) One (b) Two (c) Three

**298. At this stage of his career, Anthony Joshua was now undefeated in how many professional contests?**
(a) 13 (b) 14 (c) 15

**299. Who previously held the Commonwealth heavyweight title prior to Anthony Joshua?**
(a) David Price (b) Tyson Fury (c) Lucas Browne

**300. At the 2012 London Olympic Games, Anthony Joshua won a gold medal in which weight division?**
(a) Light-heavyweight (b) Heavyweight (c) Super-heavyweight

**301. Anthony Crolla won the WBA world lightweight crown on 21 November 2015 when he knocked out holder Darleys Perez in which round?**
(a) Three (b) Four (c) Five

**302. At this stage of his career, Anthony Crolla had now participated in how many professional contests?**
(a) 35 (b) 36 (c) 37

**303. At this stage of his career, Darleys Perez had now participated in how many professional contests?**
(a) 35 (b) 36 (c) 37

**304. What was the nationality of Darleys Perez?**
(a) Mexican (b) American (c) Columbian

**305. Where in the UK was the venue for the Crolla-Perez title contest?**
(a) Principality Stadium, Cardiff, Wales (b) Manchester Arena, Manchester, Lancashire (c) Echo Arena, Liverpool, Merseyside

**306. Tyson Fury won the WBA super version of the world heavyweight crown plus the IBF, WBO and IBO world heavyweight titles on the 28 November 2015 when he defeated defending champion Wladimir Klitschko by which method?**
(a) Five-round stoppage (b) Six-round retirement (c) 12-round points decision

**307. Who was the referee of the Fury-Klitschko contest?**
(a) Tony Weeks (b) Luis Pabon (c) Michael Griffin

**308. Where in Germany was the venue for the Fury-Klitschko title contest?**
(a) Sporthalle Alsterdorf, Hamburg (b) Esprit Arena, Dusseldorf, Nordrhein-Westfalen
(c) Kolnarena Cologne, Nordrhein-Westfallen

**309. At this stage of his career Wladimir Klitschko had now participated in how many professional contests?**
(a) 68 (b) 69 (c) 70

**310. At this stage of his career, Tyson Fury had now participated in how many professional contests?**
(a) 23 (b) 24 (c) 25

**311. On 5 December 2015, Dereck Chisora stopped his opponent Peter Erdos in which round?**
(a) Four (b) Five (c) Six

**312. Who was the referee of the Chisora-Erdos contest?**
(a) Manuel Oliver Palomo (b) Guido Cavalleri (c) Joerg Milke

**313. At this stage of his career, Dereck Chisora had now participated in how many professional contests?**
(a) 27 (b) 28 (c) 29

**314. In which country did the Chisora-Erdos contest take place?**
(a) Austria (b) England (c) Germany

**315. On 16 January 2016 David Haye stopped his opponent Mark DeMori in which round?**
(a) One (b) Two (c) Three

**316. Who was the referee of the Haye-DeMori contest?**
(a) Phil Edwards (b) Robert Williams (c) Terry O' Connor

**317. At this stage of his career, David Haye had now participated in how many professional contests?**
(a) 27 (b) 28 (c) 29

**318. Danny Garcia won the vacant WBC world welterweight crown on 23 January 2016 when he defeated opponent Robert Guerrero by which method?**
(a) Six-round stoppage (b) Nine-round knockout (c) 12-round points decision

**319. The IBF found a new world heavyweight champion on 9 April 2016 when Anthony Joshua knocked out defending title holder Charles Martin in which round?**
(a) One (b) Two (c) Three

**320. Who was the referee of the Joshua-Martin title contest?**
(a) Jean-Pierre Van Imschoot (b) Steve Gray (c) Victor Loughlin

**321. What was Charles Martin's nickname?**

(a) Lord Charles (b) Prince Charles (c) King Charles

**322. Lee Selby successfully defended his IBF world featherweight crown on 9 April 2016 when he defeated challenger Eric Hunter by which method?**

(a) Eight round knockout (c) Nine round stoppage (c) 12-round points decision

**323. During the contest Lee Selby was floored by Eric Hunter for a count in which round?**

(a) First (b) Second (c) Third

**324. On 7 May 2016 Saul Alvarez retained his WBC world middleweight crown when he knocked out challenger Amir Khan in which round?**

(a) Five (b) Six (c) Seven

**325. In which country did the Alvarez-Khan title contest take place?**

(a) Mexico (b) Canada (c) America

**326. At this stage of his career Saul Alvarez had now participated in how many professional contests?**

(a) 47 (b) 48 (c) 49

**327. At this stage of his career Amir Khan had now participated in how many professional contests?**

(a) 34 (b) 35 (c) 36

**328. Andrew Selby won the vacant British flyweight title on 14 May 2016 when he defeated opponent Louis Norman by which method?**

(a) Six-round disqualification (b) Nine-round stoppage (c) 12-round points decision

**329. At this stage of his career, Andrew Selby was now undefeated in how many professional contests?**

(a) Five (b) Six (c) Seven

**330. Who was the previous holder of the British flyweight championship prior to Andrew Selby?**

(a) Chris Edwards (b) Kevin Satchell (c) Paul Edwards

**331. Ricky Burns won the vacant WBA world super-lightweight crown on 28 May 2016 when he stopped opponent Michele Di Rocco in which round?**

(a) Seven (b) Eight (c) Nine

**332. Who was the referee of the Burns-Di Rocco title contest?**

(a) Terry O' Connor (b) Steve Gray (c) Phil Edwards

**333. On winning the WBA super-lightweight crown, Ricky Burns won his third world title in a different weight division. Which world championship had Burns not held before meeting Michele Di Rocco?**

(a) WBO featherweight (b) WBO super-featherweight (c) WBO lightweight

**334. Keith Thurman stayed on top of the WBA world welterweight throne when, on 25 June 2016, he retained his title by defeating challenger Shawn Porter by which method?**

(a) Five-round knockout (b) Eight-round disqualification (c) 12-round points decision.

**335. Who was the referee of the Thurman-Porter title contest?**

(a) Vic Drakulich (b) Steve Willis (c) Kenny Bayless

**336. Two of the ringside judges who presided at the Thurman-Porter title contest were Waleska Roldan and Steve Weisfeld. Who was the third official?**

(a) Kevin Morgan (b) Jerry Roth (c) Eric Marlinski

**337. At this stage of his career Shawn Porter had now participated in how many professional contests?**

(a) 28 (b) 29 (c) 30

**338. Terry Flanagan retained his WBO world lightweight championship on 16 July 2016 when he defeated challenger Mzonke Fana by which method?**

(a) Three-round disqualification (b) Nine-round knockout (c) 12-round points decision

**339. Terry Flanagan had now made how many successful defences of the WBO world lightweight title?**

(a) Two (b) Three (c) Four

**340. Amanda Serrano retained her WBO world female featherweight crown on 30 July 2016 when she stopped challenger Calista Silgado in which round?**

(a) One (b) Two (c) Three

**341. Who was the referee of the Serrano-Silgado title contest?**

(a) Eddie Claudio (b) Benjy Esteves jr (c) Sparkle Lee

**342. At this stage of her career, Amanda Serrano had now participated in how many professional contests?**

(a) 29 (b) 30 (c) 31

**343. Carl Frampton won the WBA super version of the world featherweight crown on 30 July 2016 when he defeated Leo Santa Cruz by which method?**

(a) Six-round knockout (b) Nine-round stoppage (c) 12-round points decision

**344. Who was the referee of the Frampton-Santa Cruz title contest?**
(a) Kenny Bayless (b) Harvey Dock (c) Jack Reiss

**345. Where in the USA did the Frampton-Santa Cruz title contest take place?**
(a) Madison Square Garden, New York (b) MGM Grand, Grand Arena, Las Vegas, Nevada (c) Barclays Center, Brooklyn, New York

**346. In which weight division did Leo Santa Cruz not hold a world title before capturing the WBA version of the super world featherweight crown?**
(a) WBO flyweight (b) IBF bantamweight (c) WBC super-bantamweight

**347. In which weight division did Carl Frampton previously hold a world crown before capturing the WBA version of the super world featherweight crown?**
(a) WBC flyweight (b) WBA & WBC bantamweight (c) WBA super version of the world super-bantamweight & IBF world super-bantamweight

**348. What was Carl Frampton's nickname?**
(a) The Tiger (b) The Jackal (c) The Bear

**349. Eduard Troyanovsky retained his IBF and IBO world super-lightweight titles against challenger Keita Obara on 9 September 2016 by a stoppage in which round?**
(a) One (b) Two (c) Three

**350. What is Eduard Troyanovsky's nickname?**
(a) The Hawk (b) The Kestrel (c) The Eagle

**351. At which venue in Russia was the Troyanovsky-Obara title contest staged?**
(a) USC Soviet Wings, Moscow (b) Khodynka Ice Palace, Moscow (c) Dynamo Palace of Sports in Krylatskoye, Moscow

**352. Dillian Whyte became the new British heavyweight champion on 7 October 2016, winning the vacant title when opponent Ian Lewison retired in which round?**
(a) 10 (b) 11 (c) 12

**353. Where in the UK was the venue for the Whyte-Lewison title contest?**
(a) O2 Arena, Greenwich, London (b) Manchester Arena, Manchester, Lancashire (c) The SEE Hydro, Glasgow, Scotland

**354. Luis Ortiz won the vacant WBA Inter-Continental heavyweight title on 12 November 2016 when he outpointed Malik Scott over 12 rounds. What is the nationality of Ortiz?**
(a) Spanish (b) Cuban (c) Argentine

**355.** *On 19 November 2016, Andre Ward won the WBA super version of the world light-heavyweight crown plus the IBF and WBO world light-heavyweight titles when he outpointed defending champion Sergey Kovalev over 12 rounds. Which world title had Ward previously held?*
(a) WBA welterweight (b) WBC and WBA middleweight (c) WBA super version and WBC super-middleweight

**356.** *Joseph Parker won the vacant WBO world heavyweight title on 10 December 2016 when he defeated opponent Andy Ruiz Jnr by which method?*
(a) Four-round knockout (b) Eight-round retirement (c) 12-round points decision

**357.** *On 10 December 2016, Jermall Charlo made a successful defence of the IBF world super-welterweight crown when he knocked out challenger Julian Williams in which round?*
(a) Five (b) Six (c) Seven

**358.** *How many defences of the IBF world super-welterweight title had Jermall Charlo now made?*
(a) Two (b) Three (c) Four

**359.** *At this stage of his career Jermall Charlo was now undefeated in how many professional contests?*
(a) 23 (b) 24 (c) 25

**360.** *Gervonta Davis won the IBF world super-featherweight title on 14 January 2017 when he stopped holder Jose Pedraza in which round?*
(a) Six (b) Seven (c) Eight

**361.** *Who was the referee of the Davis-Pedraza title contest?*
(a) Benjy Esteves jr (b) Russell Mora (c) Ricky Gonzalez

**362.** *What was the nickname of Gervonta Davis?*
(a) Tank (b) Marine (c) Commander

**363.** *On 28 January 2017 Mikey Garcia won the WBC world lightweight title when he knocked out defending champion Dejan Zlaticanin in which round?*
(a) One (b) Two (c) Three

**364.** *Where in the USA was the venue for the Garcia-Zlatičanin title contest?*
(a) Barclays Center, Brooklyn, New York (b) MGM Grand, Las Vegas, Nevada (c) Staples Center, Los Angeles, California

**365.** *At this stage of his career Mikey Garcia was now undefeated in how many professional contests?*
(a) 36 (b) 37 (c) 39

366. *A new Commonwealth flyweight champion was crowned on 24 February 2017 when Jay Harris won the crown, defeating defending title holder Thomas Essomba by which method?*
(a) Four-round disqualification (b) Eight-round knockout (c) 12-round points decision

367. *At this stage of his career Jay Harris was now undefeated in how many professional contests?*
(a) 10 (b) 11 (c) 12

368. *Jay's father Peter Harris was a former British champion in which weight division?*
(a) Flyweight (b) Bantamweight (c) Featherweight

369. *Deontay Wilder left the ring on 25 February 2017 with the WBC world heavyweight title belt still firmly strapped around his waist after stopping challenger Gerald Washington in which round?*
(a) Four (b) Five (c) Six

370. *How many successful defences of the WBC world heavyweight title had Deontay Wilder now made?*
(a) Four (b) Five (c) Six

371. *On 29 April 2017 Anthony Joshua stepped into the ring and defended his IBF world heavyweight crown and also won the vacant WBA super version of the world heavyweight title plus the vacant IBO heavyweight championship when he stopped Wladimir Klitschko in which round?*
(a) 10 (B) 11 (c) 12

372. *Who was the referee of the Joshua-Klitschko title contest?*
(a) David Fields (b) Michael Griffin (c) Eddie Cotton

373. *In which round was Wladimir Klitschko floored for the first count by Anthony Joshua during the title contest?*
(a) Three (b) Four (c) Five

374. *In which round was Anthony Joshua floored for a count by Wladimir Klitschko during the title contest?*
(a) Five (b) Five (c) Six

375. *How many times was Wladimir Klitschko floored for a count by Anthony Joshua in round 11 during the title contest?*
(a) Once (b) Twice (c) Three times

376. *Prior to challenging Anthony Joshua for the world heavyweight title, Wladimir Klitschko had participated in how many professional contests?*
(a) 68 (b) 69 (c) 70

**377. Prior to defending his title against Wladimir Klitschko, Anthony Joshua had participated in how many professional contests?**

(a) 17 (b) 18 (c) 19

**378. Wladimir Klitschko, prior to his contest with Anthony Joshua, had participated in how many world heavyweight title bouts?**

(a) 27 (b) 28 (c) 29

**379. Anthony Joshua, prior to his contest with Wladimir Klitschko, had participated in how many world heavyweight title bouts?**

(a) Three (b) Four (c) Five

**380. How many years of age was Wladimir Klitschko at the time of his title contest with Anthony Joshua?**

(a) 39 (b) 40 (c) 41

**381. How many years of age was Anthony Joshua at the time of his title contest with Wladimir Klitschko?**

(a) 27 (b) 28 (c) 29

**382.On 27 May 2017 George Groves ascended to the throne of WBA super world super-middleweight champion when he won the vacant crown by stopping his opponent Fedor Chudinov in which round?**

(a) Four (b) Five (c) Six

**383. Adonis Stevenson retained his WBC world light-heavyweight championship on 3 June 2017 when challenger Andrzej Fonfara was stopped in which round?**

(a) One (b) Two (c) Three

**384. How many successful defences of the world light-heavyweight crown had Adonis Stevenson now made?**

(a) Eight (b) Nine (c) Ten

**385. At which venue in Canada did the Stevenson-Fonfara title contest take place?**

(a) Air Canada Centre, Toronto, Ontario (b) Ricoh Coliseum, Toronto, Ontario (c) Bell Centre Montreal, Quebec

**386. What is Adonis Stevenson's nickname?**

(a) Superman (b) Batman (c) Spiderman

**387. On 4 August 2017, Claressa Shields won the WBC world female super-middleweight crown when she stopped defending title holder Nikki Adler and also picked up the vacant IBF world female super-middleweight title. In which round did the stoppage take place?**

(a) Five (b) Six (c) Seven

**388. At this stage of her career, Claressa Shields was now undefeated in how many professional contests?**

(a) Three (b) Four (c) Five

**389. On 16 September 2017, Gennady Golovkin retained the WBA super version of the world middleweight crown plus the WBC, IBF and IBO world middle titles against challenger Saul Alvarez by which method?**

(a) Three-round stoppage (b) 12-round points decision (c) A draw

**390. Joseph Parker made a successful defence of his WBO world heavyweight title on 23 September 2017 when he defeated challenger Hughie Fury by which method?**

(a) Five-round stoppage (b) Eight-round knockout (c) 12-round points decision

**391. In which country did the Parker-Fury title contest take place?**

(a) New Zealand (b) England (c) Australia

**392. At this stage of his career Joseph Parker was now undefeated in how many professional contests?**

(a) 22 (B) 23 (c) 24

**393. How many successful defences of the WBO world heavyweight championship had Joseph Parker now made?**

(a) Two (b) Three (c) Four

**394. The IBO world super-middleweight title was successfully defended by Chris Eubank Jnr on 7 October 2017 when he knocked out challenger Avni Yildirim in which round?**

(a) Three (b) Four (c) Five

**395. In which country did the Eubank Jnr-Yildirim title contest take place?**

(a) England (b) Turkey (c) Germany

**396. Going into the contest with Chris Eubank Jnr, Avni Yildirim was undefeated in how many professional contests?**

(a) 16 (b) 17 (c) 18

**397. What is the nationality of Avni Yildirim?**

(a) German (b) Turkish (c) Russian

**398. Lewis Ritson punched his way to the British lightweight title on 7 October 2017 when he stopped defending champion Robbie Barrett in which round?**

(a) Six (b) Seven (c) Eight

**399. At this stage of his career, Lewis Ritson was now undefeated in how many professional contests?**
(a) 11 (b) 12 (c) 13

**400. On 11 November 2017 Artur Beterbiev won the vacant IBF world light-heavyweight crown when he knocked out opponent Enrico Koelling in which round?**
(a) 10 (b) 11 (c) 12

**401. At this stage of his career Artur Beterbiev was now undefeated in how many professional contests?**
(a) 12 (b) 13 (c) 14

**402. In which country did the Beterbiev-Koelling title contest take place?**
(a) America (b) Germany (c) Russia

**403. What was the nationality of Artur Beterbiev?**
(a) Polish (b) Italian (c) Russian

**404. What was the nationality of Enrico Koelling?**
(a) German (b) Italian (c) Spanish

**405. Josh Taylor made a successful defence of his WBC silver super lightweight title on 11 November 2017 when he knocked out challenger Miguel Vazquez in which round?**
(a) Seven (b) Eight (c) Nine

**406. Miguel Vazquez was a former holder of which version of the world lightweight title?**
(a) IBF (b) WBA (c) WBC

**407. What was the nationality of Miguel Vazquez?**
(a) Mexican (b) American (c) Spanish

**408. Chantelle Cameron won the vacant IBO world female lightweight title on 2 December 2017 when opponent Viviane Obenauf retired in which round?**
(a) Four (b) Five (c) Six

**409. What is Chantelle Cameron's nickname?**
(a) The Fighting Rose (b) The Whisper (c) 'IlCapo'

**410. Billy Joe Saunders made a successful defence of his WBO world middleweight title on 16 December 2017 when he defeated David Lemieux by which method?**
(a) Six-round knockout (b) Nine-round disqualification (c) 12-round points decision

**411. In which country did the Saunders-Lemieux title contest take place?**
(a) Canada (b) America (c) England

**412. David Lemieux had previously held which version of the world middleweight title?**

(a) WBC (b) IBF (c) WBA

**413. Deontay Wilder successfully defended his WBC world heavyweight crown on 3 March 2018 when he stopped challenger Luis Ortiz in which round?**

(a) Eight (b) Nine (c) Ten

**414. Deontay Wilder had now made how many successful defences of the WBC world heavyweight title?**

(a) Five (b) Six (c) Seven

**415. At this stage of his career Deontay Wilder was now undefeated in how many professional contests?**

(a) 40 (b) 41 (c) 42

**416. What was Deontay Wilder's nickname?**

(a) The Bronze Bolt (b) The Bronze Bomber (c) The Bronze Destroyer

**417. On 17 March 2018, Jose Carlos Ramirez became the new WBC world super-lightweight champion when he won the vacant crown, defeating opponent Amir Ahmed Iman by which method?**

(a) Three-round stoppage (b) Six-round knockout (c) 12-round points decision.

**418. On 31 March 2018 Anthony Joshua put his WBA super version of the world heavyweight championship along with the IBF and IBO heavyweight titles on the line in a unification contest against the WBO holder Joseph Parker. Joshua emerged the victor when he defeated Parker by which method?**

(a) Six-round knockout (b) Eight-round stoppage (c) 12-round points decision.

**419. Where in the UK was the venue for the Joshua-Parker title contest?**

(a) Principality Stadium, Cardiff, Wales (b) Wembley Stadium, Wembley, London (c) Manchester Arena, Manchester, Lancashire

**420. Joseph Parker had been undefeated in how many professional contests prior to meeting Anthony Joshua?**

(a) 22 (b) 23 (c) 24

**421. Natasha Jonas won the vacant WBA international female super-featherweight title on 21 April 2018 when she stopped opponent Taoussy L' Hadji in which round?**

(a) Six (b) Seven (c) Eight

**422. Josh Warrington became the new IBF world featherweight champion when he outpointed holder Lee Selby over 12 rounds on 19 May 2018. Where in the UK was the venue for this contest?**

(a) First Direct Arena, Leeds, Yorkshire (b) Elland Road Football Ground, Leeds, Yorkshire (c) Manchester Arena, Manchester, Lancashire

**423. Going into the world title contest with Lee Selby, Josh Warrington was undefeated in how many professional contests?**

(a) 25 (b) 26 (c) 27

**424. On 26 May 2018, Kal Yafai retained his WBA world super-flyweight title when challenger David Carmona retired in round seven. In which country did the contest take place?**

(a) England (b) America (c) Mexico

**425. How many times had Kal Yafai now successfully defended the WBA world-super-flyweight championship?**

(a) Three (b) Four (c) Five

**426. At this stage of his career, Kal Yafai was now undefeated in how many professional contests?**

(a) 22 (b) 23 (c) 24

**427. On 9 June 2018 Terence Crawford relieved Jeff Horn of his WBO world welterweight crown when he stopped him in which round?**

(a) Seven (b) Eight (c) Nine

**428. At this stage of his career, Terence Crawford was now undefeated in how many professional bouts?**

(a) 33 (b) 34 (c) 35

**429. Stacey Copeland became the first holder of the Commonwealth female super-welterweight crown on 13 July 2018 when she defeated opponent Mapule Ngubane for the vacant title by which method?**

(a) Six-round stoppage (b) Eight-round knockout (c) Ten-round points decision

**430. In which country did the Copeland-Ngubane contest take place?**

(a) Uganda (b) Zimbabwe (c) England

**431. On 22 September 2018, Anthony Joshua stopped challenger Alexander Povetkin in which round in defence of his WBA super version of the world heavyweight crown plus the IBF, WBO and IBO world heavyweight titles?**

(a) Six (b) Seven (c) Eight

**432. Who was the referee of the Joshua-Povetkin world heavyweight title contest?**
(a) Giuseppe Quartarone (b) Phil Edwards (c) Steve Gray

**433. In which weight division did Alexander Povetkin win a gold medal at the 2004 Olympic Games, which took place in Athens, Greece?**
(a) Light-heavyweight (b) Heavyweight (c) Super-heavyweight

**434. Terence Crawford retained his WBO world welterweight crown on 13 October 2018 when he stopped challenger Jose Benavidez Jr in which round?**
(a) 10 (b) 11 (c) 12

**435. Lee McGregor won the vacant Commonwealth bantamweight crown on 13 October 2018 when he knocked out opponent Thomas Essomba in which round?**
(a) 10 (b) 11 (c) 12

**436. Prior to Lee McGregor, who was the previous holder of the Commonwealth bantamweight title?**
(a) Jason Moloney (b) Duke Micah (c) Jason Cunningham

**437. At this stage of his career, Lee McGregor was now undefeated in how many professional contests?**
(a) Four (b) Five (c) Six

**438. Where in the UK was Lee McGregor born?**
(a) Wales (b) England (c) Scotland

**439. Demetrius Andrade captured the vacant WBO world middleweight championship on 20 October 2018 when he outpointed opponent Walter Kautondokwa over 12 rounds. Andrade was now undefeated in how many professional contests?**
(a) 26 (b) 27 (c) 28

**440. Savannah Marshall defeated opponent Yanina Orozco on 27 October 2018 for the vacant WBA inter-continental female super-middleweight title by which method?**
(a) Six-round stoppage (b) Eight-round knockout (c) Ten-round points decision

**441. In which country did the Marshall-Orozco title contest take place?**
(a) Bulgaria (b) England (c) Italy

**442. Oleksandr Usyk stopped challenger Tony Bellew in which round on 10 November 2018 in defence of the WBA super version of the world cruiserweight crown plus the WBC, IBF and WBO world cruiserweight titles**
(a) Seven (b) Eight (c) Nine

**443. Who was the referee of the Usyk-Bellew title contest?**

(a) Ian John Lewis (b) Terry O' Connor (c) Victor Loughlin

**444. Where in the UK was the venue for the Usyk-Bellew title contest?**

(a) Manchester Arena, Manchester, Lancashire (b) O2 Arena, Greenwich, London (c) Goodison Park Stadium, Liverpool, Merseyside

**445. Tony Bellew had previously held which version of the world cruiserweight title?**

(a) WBA (b) WBC (c) WBO

**446. What was Tony Bellew's nickname?**

(a) Bomber (b) Explosive (c) Dynamite

**447. Deontay Wilder defended his WBC world heavyweight title on 1 December 2018 against challenger Tyson Fury. What was the result?**

(a) A draw (b) Points win for Wilder (c) Points win for Fury

**448. During the title contest how many times was Tyson Fury floored for a count by Deontay Wilder?**

(a) Once (b) Twice (c) Three

**449. What is the listed height of Deontay Wilder?**

(a) 6ft 5in (b) 6ft 6in (c) 6ft 7in

**450. What is the listed height of Tyson Fury?**

(a) 6ft 7in (b) 6ft 8in (c) 6ft 9in

**451. Who was the referee for the Wilder-Fury title contest?**

(a) Michael Griffin (b) Arthur Mercante Jr (c) Jack Reiss

**452. Where in America was the venue for the Wilder-Fury title contest?**

(a) Staples Center, Los Angeles, California (b) Barclays Center, Brooklyn, New York (c) MGM Grand, Grand Arena, Las Vegas

**453. Who was the reigning European heavyweight champion at the time of the Wilder-Fury title contest?**

(a) Kubrat Pulev (b) Robert Helenius (c) Agit Kabayel

**454. On 15 December 2018, Katie Taylor successfully defended her WBA and IBF world female lightweight titles when she outpointed challenger Eva Wahlstrom over ten rounds. At the time of the contest, Wahlstrom was a reigning WBC world champion in which other weight division?**

(a) Super-bantamweight (b) Featherweight (c) Super-featherweight

**455. Tony Harrison won the WBC world super-welterweight championship on 22 December 2018 when he defeated defending title holder Jermell Charlo by which method?**
(a) Six-round stoppage (b) Nine-round disqualification (c) 12-round points decision

**456. Going into the contest with Tony Harrison, Jermell Charlo was undefeated in how many professional bouts?**
(a) 30 (b) 31 (c) 32

**457. Joe Joyce stopped opponent Bermane Stiverne in round six on 23 February 2019 in defence of his Commonwealth heavyweight crown. Which version of the world heavyweight championship did Stiverne once hold?**
(a) WBA (b) WBC (c) IBF

**458. What is the nickname of Joe Joyce?**
(a) Juggernaut (b) Express Train (c) Fast Truck

**459. In which weight division did Joe Joyce win a silver medal at the 2016 Olympic games, which took place in Rio de Janeiro, Brazil?**
(a) Light-heavyweight (b) Heavyweight (c) Super-heavyweight

**460. On 24 March 2019 Christina Linardatou won the vacant WBO world female super-lightweight title, stopping opponent Kandi Wyatt in which round?**
(a) Six (b) Seven (c) Eight

**461. In which country did the Linardatou-Wyatt title contest take place?**
(a) Italy (b) Greece (c) Spain

**462. Claressa Shields defended her WBA, WBC and IBF world female middleweight championship and won the vacant WBC Diamond belt and also captured the WBO title from defending champion Christina Hammer on 13 April 2019 by which method?**
(a) Four-round stoppage (b) Seven-round retirement (c) Ten-round points decision

**463. Who was the referee of the Shields-Hammer title contest?**
(a) Sparkle Lee (b) Lou Moret (c) Thomas Taylor

**464. Claressa Shields won consecutive medals at the 2012 London, England, and 2016 Rio de Janeiro, Brazil, Olympic games, participating in the middleweight division. What colour were the respective medals?**
(a) Bronze (b) Silver (c) Gold

**465. Julian Williams won the WBA super version of the world super welterweight crown and the IBF and IBO world super-welterweight titles on 11 May 2019 when he defeated defending champion Jarrett Hurd by which method?**
(a) Four-round stoppage (b) Eight-round knockout (c) 12-round points decision.

**466. Who was the referee of the Williams-Hurd title contest?**

(a) Eddie Claudio (b) Bill Clancy (c) Lou Moret

**467. Josh Taylor took over the role of IBF world super-lightweight champion on 18 May 2019 when he defeated holder Ivan Baranchyk by which method?**

(a) Six-round stoppage (b) Nine-round disqualification (c) 12-round points decision

**468. Where in the UK was the venue for the Taylor-Baranchyk title contest?**

(a) The SSE Hydro, Glasgow, Scotland (b) O2 Arena, Greenwich, London (c) Meadowbank Sports Centre, Edinburgh, Scotland

**469. Going into the title contest with Ivan Baranchyk, Josh Taylor was undefeated in how many professional bouts?**

(a)13 (b) 14 (c) 15

**470. Going into the title contest with JoshTaylor, Ivan Baranchyk was undefeated in how many professional bouts?**

(a) 17 (b) 18 (c) 19

**471. Billy Joe Saunders became the new WBO world super-middleweight champion on 18 May 2019 when he outpointed opponent Shefat Isufi over 12 rounds. Who was the previous holder of the title?**

(a) Arthur Abraham (b) Gilberto Ramirez (c) Robert Stieglitz

**472. On 1 June 2019 Andy Ruiz Jr won the WBA super version of the world heavyweight crown plus, IBF, WBO and IBO world heavyweight titles when he stopped defending champion Anthony Joshua in which round?**

(a) Seven (b) Eight (c) Nine

**473. How many times was Andy Ruiz Jr floored for a count by Anthony Joshua during the title contest?**

(a) Once (b) Twice (c) Three

**474. How many times was Anthony Joshua floored by Andy Ruiz Jr for a count during the title contest?**

(a) Twice (b) Four (c) Five

**475. Who was the referee of the Ruiz Jr-Joshua title contest?**

(a) Tony Weeks (b) David Fields (c) Michael Griffin

**476. What is Andy Ruiz Jr's nickname?**

(a) Destroyer (b) Warrior (c) Mexican Storm

**477. Two of the three ringside judges present at the Ruiz Jr-Joshua title contest was Michael Alexander, Pasquale Procopio. Who was the third official?**
(a) Julie Lederman (b) Pawel Kardyni (c) Carlos Sucre

**478. Where in the USA was the venue for the Ruiz Jr-Joshua title contest?**
(a) Barclays Centre, Brooklyn, New York (b) Madison Square Garden, New York
(c) MGM Grand, Grand Garden Arena, Las Vegas, Nevada

**479. Katie Taylor retained her WBA, IBF and WBO world female lightweight titles and won the WBC crown from the defending champion Delfine Persoon on 1 June 2019 by which method?**
(a) Three-round stoppage (b) Nine-round knockout (c) Ten-round points decision

**480. Who was the referee of the Taylor-Persoon title contest?**
(a) Sparkle Lee (b) Leo Gerstel (c) Benjy Esteves Jr

**481. Callum Smith made a successful first defence of his WBA super world super-middleweight championship and a third defence of the WBC super-middleweight Diamond title on 1 June 2019 when he stopped challenger Hassan N' Dam N'Jikam in which round?**
(a) Two (b) Three (c) Four

**482. At this stage of his career Callum Smith was now undefeated in how many professional contests?**
(a) 26 (b) 27 (c) 28

**483. Jay Harris became the new European flyweight champion on 1 June 2019, outpointing opponent Angel Moreno over 12 rounds to win the vacant title. Where in the UK was the venue for this contest?**
(a) York Hall, Bethnal Green, London (b) Vale Sports Arena, Cardiff, Wales (c) Ice Arena, Cardiff, Wales

**484. Zelfa Barrett won the vacant Commonwealth super-featherweight crown on 15 June 2019 when he defeated opponent Leon Woodstock by which method?**
(a) Four-round disqualification (b) Nine-round stoppage (c) 12-round points decision

**485. Prior to Zelfa Barrett, who was the previous holder of the Commonwealth super-featherweight title?**
(a) Martin Joseph Ward (b) James Tennyson (c) Andy Townend

**486. Daniel Dubois won the vacant British heavyweight title on 13 July 2019 when he knocked out opponent Nathan Gorman in which round?**
(a) Five (b) Six (c) Seven

**487. Going into the contest with Nathan Gorman, Daniel Dubois was undefeated in how many professional contests?**

(a) 10 (b) 11 (c) 12

**488. Going into the contest with Daniel Dubois, Nathan Gorman was undefeated in how many professional contests?**

(a)16 (b) 17 (c) 18

**489. How many years of age was Daniel Dubois at the time of the title contest with Nathan Gorman?**

(a) 21 (b) 22 (c) 23

**490. How many years of age was Nathan Gorman at the time of the title contest with Daniel Dubois?**

(a) 22 (b) 23 (c) 24

**491. Who was the previous holder of the British heavyweight title prior to Daniel Dubois?**

(a) Hughie Fury (b) Sam Sexton (c) Dillian Whyte

**492. Terri Harper won the vacant IBO world female super-featherweight crown on 19 July 2019 when she stopped her opponent Nozipho Bell in which round?**

(a) Nine (b) Eight (c) Ten

**493. How many years of age was Terri Harper at the time of the Nozipho Bell title contest?**

(a) 22 (b) 23 (c) 24

**494. Chantelle Cameron retained her WBC Silver female lightweight title on 20 July 2019 when she outpointed challenger Anisha Basheel over ten rounds. At this stage of her career Cameron was now undefeated in how many professional contests?**

(a) 10 (b) 11 (c) 12

**495. Dereck Chisora knocked out opponent Artur Szpilka in round two on 20 July 2019. Szpilka had on 16 January 2016 stepped up to challenge Deontay Wilder for the WBC world heavyweight crown and failed in his bid when knocked out in which round?**

(a) Eight (b) Nine (c) Ten

**496. What is the nationality of Artur Szpilka?**

(a) German (b) Polish (c) Bulgarian

**497. Kosei Tanaka retained his WBO world flyweight crown on 24 August 2019, stopping his challenger Jonathan Gonzalez in which round?**

(a) Six (b) Seven (c) Eight

**498. In which country did the Tanaka-Gonzalez title contest take place?**
(a) Japan (b) Mexico (c) America

**499. Kosei Tanaka had now made how many successful defences of the WBO world flyweight title?**
(a) Two (b) Three (c) Four

**500. At this stage of his career Kosei Tanaka was now undefeated in how many professional contests?**
(a) 14 (b) 15 (c) 16

**501. On 24 August 2019 Sergey Kovalev made a successful defence of his WBO world light-heavyweight crown stopping challenger Anthony Yarde in which round?**
(a) Nine (b) Ten (c) 11

**502. Going into the title contest with Sergey Kovalev, Anthony Yarde was undefeated in how many professional contests?**
(a) 18 (b) 19 (c) 20

**503. What was Sergey Kovalev's nickname?**
(a) Terminator (b) Krusher (c) Iron Fist

**504. Who was the referee of the Kovalev-Yarde title contest?**
(a) Robert Byrd (b) Steve Willis (c) Luis Pabon

**505. In which country did the Kovalev-Yarde title contest take place?**
(a) America (b) Russia (c) England

**506. Vasiliy Lomachenko retained the WBA super version of the world lightweight crown plus the WBO world lightweight title and also won the vacant WBC world lightweight crown on 31 August 2019 when he defeated Luke Campbell on points over 12 rounds. In which round was Campbell floored for a count by Lomachenko count?**
(a) 10 (b) 11 (c) 12

**507. At the 2012 London, England, Olympic Games Luke Campbell won a gold medal in which weight division?**
(a) Flyweight (b) Bantamweight (c) Featherweight

**508. On 13 September 2019 Amanda Serrano won the WBO world featherweight crown when she defeated defending champion Heather Hardy and in so doing also captured the vacant WBC interim version of the title by which method?**
(a) Four-round stoppage (b) Six-round knockout (c) Ten-round points decision

**509. Daniel Dubois won the vacant Commonwealth heavyweight crown and the vacant WBO International heavyweight title on 27 September 2019 when he stopped opponent Ebenezer Tetteh in which round?**
(a) One (b) Two (c) Three

**510. Going into the contest with Daniel Dubois, Ebenezer Tetteh was undefeated in how many professional contests?**
(a) 18 (b) 19 (c) 20

**511. Nicola Adams retained her WBO world female flyweight title on 27 September 2019 against challenger Maria Salinas by which method?**
(a) Four-round stoppage (b) Ten-round points decision (c) A draw

**512. Nicola Adams had proved successful at the Olympic Games which had taken place in London, England, 2012 and Rio de Janeiro, Brazil, 2016, winning a medal in the flyweight division. What was the colour of the respective medals?**
(a) Bronze (b) Silver (c) Gold

**513. A world welterweight unification contest took place on 28 September 2019 when Errol Spence Jr the IBF king met WBC holder Shawn Porter and emerged victorious when outpointing his opponent over 12 rounds. At this stage of his career, Spence Jr was now undefeated in how many professional contests?**
(a) 25 (b) 26 (c) 27

**514. On 5 October 2019 Gennady Golovkin crossed gloves with opponent Sergiy Derevyanchenko in a contest for the vacant IBF and IBO world middleweight titles. What was the result in a bout which went the full 12 rounds?**
(a) Points win for Golovkin (b) Points win for Derevyanchenko (c) A draw

**515. Josh Warrington made a successful defence of his IBF world featherweight crown on 12 October 2019 when he stopped challenger Sofiane Takoucht in which round?**
(a) One (b) Two (c) Three

**515. At this stage of his career, Josh Warrington was undefeated in how many professional contests?**
(a) 30 (b) 31 (c) 32

**517. Who was the referee of the Warrington-Takoucht title contest?**
(a) Michael Alexander (b) Steve Gray (c) Robert Williams

**518. In a world light-heavyweight unification contest on 18 October 2019, Artur Beterbiev the IBF title holder met WBC counterpart Oleksandr Gvozdyk and emerged victorious stopping his opponent in which round?**
(a) 10 (b) 11 (c) 12

*519. On 19 October 2019 Savannah Marshall stopped her opponent Ashleigh Curry in three rounds. What is Marshall's nickname?*

(a) Whispering Assassin (b) Silent Assassin (c) Quiet Assassin

*520. Shakur Stevenson won the vacant WBO world featherweight title on 26 October 2019, outpointing opponent Joet Gonzalez over 12 rounds. At this stage of his career Stevenson was now undefeated in how many professional contests?*

(a) 13 (b) 14 (c) 15

*521. Shakur Stevenson won a silver medal in which weight division at the 2016 Olympic Games, which were staged in Rio de Janeiro, Brazil?*

(a) Flyweight (b) Bantamweight (c) Featherweight

*522. On 26 October 2019 Josh Taylor retained his IBF world super-lightweight title and won the WBA super version of the super-lightweight crown from defending champion Regis Prograis in a unification contest by which method?*

(a) Six-round stoppage (b) Nine-round retirement (c) 12-round points decision

*523. Who was Josh Taylor's trainer for the Regis-Prograis title contest?*

(a) Shane McGuigan (b) Adam Booth (c) Robert McCracken

*524. Lawrence Okolie won the European cruiserweight crown on 26 October 2019 when he stopped defending title holder Yves Ngabu in which round?*

(a) Seven (b) Eight (c) Nine

*525. At this stage of his career Lawrence Okolie was now undefeated in how many professional contests?*

(a) 13 (b) 14 (c) 15

*526. Prior to Lawrence Okolie how many British boxers had previously held the European cruiserweight crown?*

(a) Six (b) Seven (c) Eight

*527. Saul Alvarez took the WBO world light-heavyweight crown on 2 November 2019 when he knocked out defending title holder Sergey Kovalev in round 11. Two of the three ringside judges present were Dave Moretti and Don Trella. Who was the third official?*

(a) Adalaide Byrd (b) Julie Lederman (c) Lynne Carter

*528. Felix Cash made a successful defence of his Commonwealth middleweight crown on 2 November 2019 when he stopped challenger Jack Cullen in which round?*

(a) Eight (b) Nine (c) Ten

**529. At this stage of his career, Felix Cash was now undefeated in how many professional contests?**

(a) 10 (b) 11 (c) 12

**530. On 2 November 2019, Katie Taylor captured the WBO world female super-lightweight title when she outpointed defending champion Christina Linardatou over ten rounds. At this stage of her career Taylor was now undefeated in how many professional contests?**

(a) 13 (b) 14 (c) 15

**531. Katie Taylor competed at the 2012 London, England, Olympic Games, winning which colour medal in the lightweight division?**

(a) Bronze (b) Silver (c) Gold

**532. In a unification contest on 7 November 2019, Naoya Inoue successfully defended his IBF world bantamweight crown and also won the WBA super version of the world bantamweight title from Nonito Donaire by which method?**

(a) Ten stoppage (b) Eleven-round knockout (c) 12-round points decision

**533. Who was the referee of the Inoue-Donaire title contest?**

(a) Ernie Sharif (b) Luis Pabon (c) Pinit Prayadsab

**534. In which round was Nonito Donaire floored for a count by Naoya Inoue during the title contest?**

(a) 10 (b) 11 (c) 12

**535. At this stage of his career Naoya Inoue was now undefeated in how many professional contests?**

(a) 19 (b) 20 (c) 21

**536. At this stage of his career, Nonito Donaire had now participated in how many professional contests?**

(a) 45 (b) 46 (c) 47

**537. What was Nonito Donaire's nickname?**

(a) The Filipino Storm (b) The Filipino Flash (c) The Filipino Hurricane

**538. What was Naoya Inoue's nickname?**

(a) Monster (b) Invader (c) Crusher

**539. Nordine Oubaali successfully retained his WBC world bantamweight title on 7 November 2019 when he defeated challenger Takuma Inoue by a 12-round points decision. In which country did this contest take place?**

(a) Japan (b) France (c) Thailand

**540. How many successful defences of the WBC world bantamweight title had Nordine Oubaali now made?**
(a) One (b) Two (c) Three

**541. What was the nationality of Nordine Oubaali?**
(a) Italian (b) French (c) Spanish

**542. What was the nationality of Takuma Inoue?**
(a) Japanese (b) American (c) South Korean

**543. On 9 November 2019 Billy Joe Saunders retained his WBO world super-middleweight crown when he knocked out challenger Marcelo Esteban Coceres in which round?**
(a) Six (b) Nine (c) 11

**544. In which USA venue did the Saunders-Coceres title contest take place?**
(a) Barclays Center, Brooklyn, New York (b) Staples Center, Los Angeles, California
(c) MGM Grand, Grand Garden Arena, Las Vegas, Nevada

**545. Who was the referee of the Saunders-Coceres title contest?**
(a) Ray Corona (b) Jack Reiss (c) Kenny Bayless

**546. Two of the three judges present at ringside for the Saunders-Coceres title contest were Lou Moret and Robin Taylor, but who was the third official?**
(a) David Hudson (b) Lisa Giampa (c) Patricia Morse Jarman

**547. What was the nationality of Marcelo Esteban Coceres?**
(a) Argentine (b) Mexican (c) Italian

**548. Chantelle Cameron outpointed opponent Anahi Ester Sanchez over ten rounds on 9 November 2019. At this stage of her career Cameron was now undefeated in how many professional contests?**
(a) 10 (b) 11 (c) 12

**549. Kubrat Pulev outpointed his opponent Rydell Booker over ten rounds on 9 November 2019. How many professional contests had Pulev now participated in?**
(a) 29 (b) 30 (c) 31

**550. How many bouts had Kubrat Pulev indulged in during the course of 2019?**
(a) Two (b) Three (c) Four

**551. A successful defence of the WBA Oceania bantamweight crown was made by defending champion Jason Moloney on 15 November 2019 when he knocked out challenger Dixon Flores in which round?**
(a) One (b) Two (c) Three

**552. Which venue in Australia did the Moloney-flores title contest take place?**

(a) Margaret Court Arena, Melbourne, Victoria (b) Seagulls Rugby League Club, Tweeds Heads, New South Wales (c) Function Centre, Melbourne Park, Victoria

**553. On 16 November 2019 Lee McGregor successfully defended his Commonwealth bantamweight title and won the British bantamweight crown from holder Ukashir Farooq by which method?**

(a) Three-round stoppage (b) Nine-round knockout (c) 12-round points decision

**554. At the time of the McGregor-Farooq title contest, who was the reigning European bantamweight Champion?**

(a) Karim Guerfi (b) Georges Ory (c) Ryan Farrag

**555. Yamileth Mercado won the WBC world female super-bantamweight crown when she outpointed holder Fatuma Zarika over ten rounds on 16 November 2019. In which country did the title contest take place?**

(a) Mexico (b) Kenya (c) Uganda

**556. What is the nationality of Yamileth Mercado?**

(a) American (b) Mexican (c) Nicaraguan

**557. What is the nationality of Fatuma Zarika?**

(a) Kenyan (b) German (c) Austrian

**558. On 22 November 2019 Jack Catterall defeated opponent Timo Schwarzkopf on points over how many rounds?**

(a) Six (b) Eight (c) Ten

**559. At this stage of his career Jack Catterall was now undefeated in how many professional contests?**

(a) 25 (b) 26 (c) 27

**560. At the time of his contest with Timo Schwarzkopf, Jack Catterall was a former British champion in which weight division?**

(a) Lightweight (b) Super-lightweight (c) Welterweight

**561. In which country did the Catterall-Schwarzkopf contest take place?**

(a) United Arab Emirates (b) Germany (c) England

**562. At this stage of his career, Timo Schwarzkopf had now participated in how many professional contests?**

(a) 22 (b) 23 (c) 24

*563. Callum Smith successfully defended the super version of the WBA super-middleweight crown and also retained the WBC Diamond super-middleweight title on 23 November 2019, defeating his challenger John Ryder by which method?*
(a) Five-round disqualification (b) Nine-round stoppage (c) 12-round points decision

*564. A new Commonwealth cruiserweight champion was crowned on 23 November 2019 when Chris Billam-Smith won the vacant title, stopping opponent Craig Glover in which round?*
(a) Five (b) Six (c) Seven

*565. Who was the referee of the Billiam-Smith-Glover title contest?*
(a) Terry O'Connor (b) Mark Lyson (c) Marcus McDonnell

*566. Deontay Wilder made a successful defence of the WBC world heavyweight title on 23 November 2019, knocking out challenger Luis Ortiz in which round?*
(a) Five (b) Six (c) Seven

*567. At which American venue did the Wilder-Ortiz title contest take place?*
(a) MGM Grand, Grand Garden Arena, Las Vegas, Nevada (b) Staples Center, Los Angeles, California (c) Barclays Center, Brooklyn, New York

*568. How many times had Deontay Wilder now successfully defended the WBC world heavyweight title?*
(a) 10 (b) 11 (c) 12

*569. Cecilia Braekhus retained her WBC, WBA, IBF, WBO and IBO world female welterweight titles on 30 November 2019 when she defeated challenger Victoria Noelia Bustos by which method?*
(a) Six-round stoppage (b) Nine-round retirement (c) Ten-round points decision

*570. Who was the referee of the Braekhus-Bustos title contest?*
(a) Sparkle Lee (b) Diana Milani (c) Phil Edwards

*571. On 30 November 2019, Zhilei Zhang successfully defended his WBO Oriental heavyweight title against Andriy Rudenko, defeating him by which method?*
(a) Eight-round stoppage (b) Nine-round disqualification (c) Ten-round points decision

*572. At this stage of his career, Zhilei Zhang was now undefeated in how many professional contests*
(a) 20 (b) 21 (c) 22

*573. Prior to his contest with Andriy Rudenko, Zhilei Zhang had won how many of his previous bouts inside the scheduled distance, be it by a knockout or stoppage?*
(a) 16 (b) 17 (c) 18

574. *What was the listed height of Zhilei Zhang?*
(a) 6ft 4in (b) 6ft 5in (c) 6ft 6in

575. *Two of the three judges present at the ringside for the Zhang-Rudenko title contest were Ferenc Budai and Stephane Nicolo. Who was the third official?*
(a) Kevin Morgan (b) Gloria Martinez-Rizzo (c) Debra Barnes

576. *What was the nationality of Zhilei Zhang?*
(a) Chinese (b) Japanese (c) South Korean

577. *John Riel Casimero captured the WBO world bantamweight crown on 30 November 2019 when he stopped defending champion Zolani Tete in which round?*
(a) One (b) Two (c) Three

578. *Carl Frampton punched his way to a points decision on 30 November 2019 over opponent Tyler McCreary. Over how many rounds was the fight scheduled?*
(a) Eight (b) Ten (c) 12

579. *At this stage of his career Carl Frampton had now participated in how many professional contests?*
(a) 27 (b) 28 (c) 29

580. *On 7 December 2019, Jermall Charlo put his WBC world middleweight crown on the line against challenger Dennis Hogan and proved successful in his defence when retaining the title by a stoppage in which round?*
(a) Six (b) Seven (c) Eight

581. *Anthony Joshua regained the super version of the WBA world heavyweight crown plus the IBF, WBO and IBO world heavyweight titles on 7 December 2019 when he defeated defending champion Andy Ruiz Jr by which method?*
(a) Six-round stoppage (b) Nine-round knockout (c) 12-round points decision

582. *Who was the referee of the Joshua-Ruiz Jr title contest?*
(a) David Fields (b) Luis Pabon (c) Kenny Bayless

583. *How many world heavyweight title bouts had Anthony Joshua now participated in?*
(a) Nine (b) Ten (c) 11

584. *In which country did the Joshua-Ruiz Jr title contest take place?*
(a) Saudia Arabia (b) Mexico (c) America

585. *Dillian Whyte outpointed opponent Mariusz Wach over ten rounds on 7 December 2019. What is Whyte's nickname?*
(a) The Finisher (b) The Body Snatcher (c) The Head Hunter

*586. Teofimo Lopez entered the ring as a challenger for the IBF world lightweight title on 14 December 2019 and later made his exit as the new title holder when he took the crown from defending champion Richard Commey, stopping him in which round?*

(a) One (b) Two (c) Three

*587. Two of the three judges present at ringside for the Commey-Lopez title contest were Julie Lederman and Eric Marlinski. Who was the third official?*

(a) Larry Hazzard Jr (b) Steve Weisfeld (c) Ron McNair

*588. Terence Crawford retained his WBO world welterweight title on 14 December 2019 when he stopped his challenger Egidijus Kavaliauskas in which round?*

(a) Seven (b) Eight (c) Nine

*589. Guadalupe Martinez Guzman successfully retained her WBC world female super-flyweight title on 14 December 2019 when she defeated challenger Debani Balderas by which method?*

(a) Four-round stoppage (b) Seven-round knockout (c) Ten-round points decision

*590. Richard Riakporhe won the vacant British cruiserweight crown on 19 December 2019 when he outpointed opponent Jack Massey over 12 rounds. At this stage of his career Riakporhe was now undefeated in how many professional contests?*

(a) ten (b) 11 (c) 12

*591. Daniel Dubois knocked out opponent Kyotaro Fujimoto in two rounds on 21 December 2019 in defence of his WBO International heavyweight title and for the vacant WBC Silver heavyweight crown. Who held the WBC Silver heavyweight title prior to Dubois?*

(a) Dillian Whyte (b) Johann Duhaupas (c) Alexander Povetkin

*592. Sunny Edwards entered the ring on 21 December 2019 to contest the vacant British super-flyweight crown and became the new champion when he defeated opponent Marcel Braithwaite by which method?*

(a) Two-round stoppage (b) Eight-round knockout (c) 12-round points decision

*593. Who held the British super-flyweight title prior to Sunny Edwards?*

(a) Kal Yafai (b) Charlie Edwards (c) Paul Butler

*594. On 8 February 2020 Terri Harper successfully defended her IBO super-featherweight title and won the WBC version of the championship when she defeated holder Eva Wahlstrom by which method?*

(a) Four-round stoppage (b) Eight-round knockout (c) Ten-round points decision

**595. Tyson Fury won the WBC world heavyweight championship on 22 February 2020 when he stopped defending title holder Deontay Wilder in which round?**
(a) Seven (b) Eight (c) Nine

**596. How many times was Deontay Wilder floored for a count by Tyson Fury during the title contest?**
(a) Twice (b) Three (c) Four

**597. Who was the referee of the Tyson-Wilder title contest?**
(a) Kenny Bayless (b) Tony Weeks (c) Jack Reiss

**598. Where in America was the venue for the Tyson-Wilder title contest?**
(a) T-Mobile Arena, Las Vegas, Nevada (b) Staples Center, Los Angeles, California
(c) MGM Grand, Grand Garden Arena, Las Vegas, Nevada

**599. Kal Yafai lost his WBA world super-flyweight title on 29 February 2020 when he was stopped in which round by challenger Roman Gonzalez?**
(a) Seven (b) Eight (c) Nine

**600. In which country did the Yafai-Gonzalez title contest take place?**
(a) America (b) France (c) Italy

**601. Julio Cesar Martinez made a successful defence of his WBC world flyweight title on 29 February 2020 when he defeated his challenger Jay Harris by which method?**
(a) Six-round knockout (b) Nine-round disqualification (b) 12-round points decision

**602. Who was the referee of the Martinez-Harris title contest?**
(a) Raul Caiz Jr (b) Laurence Cole (c) Hector Afu

**603. How many times had Julio Cesar Martinez by then defended the WBC world flyweight championship?**
(a) Once (b) Twice (c) Three times

**604. On 9 June 2020 Shakur Stevenson knocked out his opponent Felix Caraballo in which round?**
(a) Four (b) Five (c) Six

**605. How many rounds was the Stevenson-Caraballo contest scheduled for?**
(a) Eight (b) Ten (c) 12

**606. Who was the referee of the Stevenson-Caraballo contest?**
(a) Tony Weeks (b) David Fields (c) Gary Rosato

**607. Jason Moloney won his contest against opponent Leonard Baez on 25 June 2020 by a retirement in which round?**
(a) Six (b) Seven (c) Eight

**608. In which country did the Moloney-Baez contest take place?**
(a) America (b) Australia (c) Canada

**609. On 9 July 2020 Carlos Takam and Jerry Forrest stepped into the ring to meet in a ten-round contest. What was the result?**
(a) Points win for Forrest (b) Points win for Takam (c) A draw

**610. By which method did Brad Foster retain his British and Commonwealth super-bantamweight titles against challenger James Beech Jr on 10 July 2020?**
(a) Eight-round stoppage (b) Ten-round knockout (c) 12-round points decision.

**611. What is Brad Foster's nickname?**
(a) The Blade (b) The Sword (c) The Lance

**612. Who was the referee of the Foster-Beech Jr title contest?**
(a) Phil Edwards (b) Marcus McDonnell (c) Mark Lyson

**613. Mikaela Mayer defeated opponent Helen Joseph on 14 July 2020 when she outpointed her over how many rounds?**
(a) Six (b) Eight (c) Ten

**614. Two of the three judges present at ringside for the Mayer-Joseph contest were Patricia Morse Jarman and Dave Moretti. Who was the third?**
(a) Lisa Giampa (b) Julie Lederman (c) Jeff Sinnett

**615. On 18 July 2020 Agit Kabayel outpointed opponent Evgenios Lazaridis over ten rounds to capture the vacant WBA Continental heavyweight crown. Who was the previous holder of this championship?**
(a) Joe Joyce (b) Alexander Povetkin (c) David Price

**616. In which country did the Kabayel-Lazaridis title contest take place?**
(a) Poland (b) Germany (c) America

**617. At this stage of his career Agit Kabayel was undefeated in how many professional contests?**
(a) 20 (b) 21 (c) 22

**618. In which year did Agit Kabayel make his professional debut?**
(a) 2011 (b) 2012 (c) 2013

**619. Oscar Valdez stopped his opponent Jayson Velez in which round on 21 July 2020?**
(a) Eight (b) Nine (c) Ten

**620. Who was the referee of the Valdez-Velez contest?**
(a) Tony Weeks (b) Russell Mora (c) Vic Drakulich

*621. At this stage of his career Oscar Valdez was now undefeated in how many professional contests?*

(a) 27 (b) 28 (c) 29

*622. On 25 July 2020 Joe Joyce stopped his opponent Michael Wallisch in which round?*

(a) One (b) Two (c) Three

*623. In a contest for the vacant Japanese light-flyweight championship, which took place on 26 July 2020, Masamichi Yabuki became the new title holder when he knocked out his opponent Tsuyoshi Sato in which round?*

(a) One (b) Two (c) Three

*624. Who was the referee of the Yabuki-Sato title contest?*

(a) Charlie Choi (b) Michiaki Someya (c) Nobuto Ikehara

*625. Where in Japan was the venue for the Yabuki-Sato title contest?*

(a) Aioi Hall, Kariya, Aichi (b) Korakuen Hall, Tokyo (c) Suntopia, Soja, Okayama

*626. Lyndon Arthur made a successful defence of his Commonwealth light-heavyweight crown on 31 July 2020 when he defeated his challenger Dec Spelman by which method?*

(a) Four-round stoppage (b) Eight-round knockout (c) 12-round points decision

*627. At this stage of his career, Lyndon Arthur was now undefeated in how many professional contests?*

(a) 17 (b) 18 (c) 19

*628. What was Lyndon Arthur's nickname?*

(a) Prince Arthur (b) King Arthur (d) Lord Arthur

*629. On 1 August 2020 Ted Cheeseman became the new IBF international super-welterweight champion when he defeated the defending title holder Sam Eggington by which method?*

(a) Six-round stoppage (b) Nine-round knockout (c) 12-round points decision

*630. In which weight division had Sam Eggington previously held a European title?*

(a) Welterweight (b) Super-welterweight (c) Middleweight

*631. The vacant British lightweight title found a new holder when James Tennyson stopped his opponent Gavin Gwynne in which round on 1 August 2020 to win the championship?*

(a) One (b) Six (c) Nine

**632. James Tennyson was a former European champion in which weight division?**
(a) Featherweight (b) Super-featherweight (c) Lightweight

**633. Fabio Wardley stepped into the ring on 1 August 2020 to contest the vacant English heavyweight title and secured the championship when he stopped his opponent Simon Vallily in the third round. Prior to Wardley, who was the previous holder of the title?**
(a) Daniel Dubois (a) David Price (c) John McDermott

**634. At this stage of his career Fabio Wardley was now undefeated in how many professional contests?**
(a) Eight (b) Nine (c) Ten

**635. On 1 August 2020 Jordan Gill boxed his way to a ten-round points decision over his opponent Reece Bellotti. Both had previously been a holder of which championship in the featherweight division?**
(a) British (b) European (c) Commonwealth

**636. Angelo Leo and Tramaine Williams met on 1 August 2020 in a contest for the vacant WBO world super-bantamweight title. Leo won the crown when he defeated his opponent by which method?**
(a) Four-round disqualification (b) Nine-round stoppage (c) 12-round points decision

**637. Who was the referee of the Leo-Williams world title contest?**
(a) Kenny Bayless (b) Harvey Dock (c) Jim Korb

**638. At this stage of his career Angelo Leo was now undefeated in how many professional contests?**
(a) 20 (b) 21 (c) 22

**639. At the time of the Leo-Williams title contest who was the female holder of the WBO world super-bantamweight crown?**
(a) Dina Thorslund (b) Amanda Serrano (c) Sabrina Maribel Perez

**640. Terri Harper retained her WBC and IBO world female super-featherweight titles on 7 August 2020 against challenger Natasha Jonas by which method?**
(a) Four-round stoppage (b) Ten-round points decision (c) Ten-round draw

**641. At this stage of her career Terri Harper had now participated in how many professional contests?**
(a) 10 (b) 11 (c) 12

**642. At this stage of her career Natasha Jonas had participated in how many professional contests?**
(a) 11 (b) 12 (c) 13

**643. Who was the trainer of Terri Harper at the time of the title contest?**
(a) Peter Fury (b) Mark Tibbs (c) Stefy Bull

**644. Who was the trainer of Natasha Jonas at the time of the title contest?**
(a) Joe Gallagher (b) Dominic Ingle (c) Shane McGuigan

**645. Who was the referee of the Harper-Jonas title contest?**
(a) John Latham (b) Victor Loughlin (c) Marcus McDonnell

**646. At the 2012 AIBA Women's World boxing Championships, which took place in Qinhuangdao, China, Natasha Jonas competed in the lightweight division and won which colour medal?**
(a) Bronze (b) Silver (c) Gold

**647. On 7 August 2020 Chris Billam-Smith retained his Commonwealth cruiserweight title when he stopped his challenger Nathan Thorley in which round?**
(a) Two (b) Three (c) Four

**648. Anthony Fowler stopped his opponent Adam Harper in round seven of a bout scheduled for ten on 7 August 2020. During his stint in the amateur code, Fowler fought at the 2014 Commonwealth games, which were held in Glasgow, Scotland. Fowler competed at middleweight and won which colour medal?**
(a) Bronze (b) Silver (c) Gold

**649. On 8 August 2020 Kerman Lejarraga outpointed opponent Tyrone Nurse over how many rounds?**
(a) Six (b) Eight (c) Ten

**650. In which country did the Lejarraga-Nurse contest take place?**
(a) Germany (b) Spain (c) Italy

**651. At the time of the contest Kerman Lejarraga was a former European champion in which weight division?**
(a) Lightweight (b) Super-lightweight (c) Welterweight

**652. At the time of the contest Tyrone Nurse was a former British champion in which weight division?**
(a) Lightweight (b) Super-lightweight (c) Welterweight

**653. Toshiki Shimomachi retained his Japanese youth super-bantamweight title on 9 August 2020 when he stopped challenger Hiroki Hanabusa in which round?**
(a) Five (b) Six (c) Seven

**654. In which capacity is Michael Buffer involved with boxing?**
(a) Referee (b) Master of ceremonies (c) Judge

**655. What is the nationality of Buffer?**
(a) Canadian (b) American (c) Australian

**656. What is Tyson Fury's middle name?**
(a) Luke (b) Paul (c) David

**657. Ryo Sagawa successfully defended his Japanese featherweight title on 13 August 2020 when he knocked out his challenger Yuri Takemoto in which round?**
(a) Five (b) Six (c) Seven

**658. On 14 August 2020 Zelfa Barrett stepped into the ring to contest the vacant IBF intercontinental super-featherweight crown and emerged victorious when he stopped his opponent Eric Donovan in which round?**
(a) Seven (b) Eight (c) Nine

**659. Prior to Zelfa Barrett, who was the former holder of the IBF intercontinental super-featherweight title?**
(a) Devis Boschiero (b) Azinga Fuzile (c) Jono Carroll

**660. Felix Cash retained his Commonwealth middleweight title on 14 August 2020 when he stopped challenger Jason Welborn in which round?**
(a) Five (b) Six (c) Seven

**661. In which weight division was Jason Welborn a former British champion?**
(a) Welterweight (b) Super-welterweight (c) Middleweight

**662. Rachel Ball and Shannon Courtenay exchanged punches on 14 August 2020 in a contest which saw Ball winning a points decision over how many rounds?**
(a) Six (B) Eight (c) Ten

**663. In which round was Shannon Courtenay floored for a count by Rachel Ball during the contest?**
(a) One (b) Two (c) Three

**664. Going into the contest with Rachel Ball, Shannon Courtenay was undefeated in how many professional bouts?**
(a) Four (b) Five (c) Six

**665. On 15 August 2020 Carl Frampton defeated his opponent Darren Traynor when he stopped him in which round?**
(a) Five (b) Six (c) Seven

**666. In which round was Darren Traynor floored for a count by Carl Frampton during the contest?**
(a) Four (c) Five (c) Six

*667. Michael Conlan stopped his opponent Sofiane Takoucht in which round on 15 August 2020?*

(a) Eight (b) Nine (c) Ten

*668. At this stage of his career Michael Conlan was now undefeated in how many professional contests?*

(a) 14 (b) 15 (c) 16

*669. Jessica McCaskill won the WBC, WBA, IBF, WBO, IBO female world welterweight titles on 15 August 2020 when she defeated holder Cecilia Braekhus by which method?*

(a) Eight-round stoppage (b) Nine-round knockout (c) Ten-round points decision

*670. Prior to meeting Jessica McCaskill, Cecilia Braekhus had been undefeated in how many professional contests?*

(a) 36 (b) 37 (c) 38

*671. How many world title bouts had Cecilia Braekhus now taken part in?*

(a) 26 (b) 27 (c) 28

*672. Two of the three judges present at ringside for the Braekhus-McCaskill title contest were Gerald Ritter and David Sutherland, but who was the third official?*

(a) Mike Ross (b) Karen Holderfield (c) Levi Martinez

*673. In which country did the Braekhus-McCaskill contest take place?*

(a) Mexico (b) Canada (c) America

*674. Which one of the following boxers was not born in Scotland?*

(a) Shannon Courtenay (b) Hannah Rankin (c) Kristen Fraser

*675. Shakan Pitters stepped between the ropes on 22 August 2020 to contest the vacant British light-heavyweight title and emerged victorious when he defeated opponent Chad Sugden by which method?*

(a) Four-round stoppage (b) Six-round knockout (c) 12-round points decision.

*676. At this stage of his career Shakan Pitters was now undefeated in how many professional contests?*

(a) 14 (b) 15 (c) 16

*677. Isaac Chamberlain stepped into the ring on 22 August 2020 and stopped his opponent Antony Woolery in which round?*

(a) Two (b) Three (c) Four

*678 Katie Taylor had a successful night on 22 August 2020 when she retained her WBC, WBA, IBF and WBO female world lightweight titles against challenger Delfine Persoon by which method?*

(a) Six-round stoppage (b) Eight-round retirement (c) Ten-round points decision

*679. At this stage of her professional career Katie Taylor had now participated in how many world title contests?*

(a) Eight (b) Nine (c) Ten

*680. At the time of her contest with Katie Taylor what was the occupation of Belgium's Delfine Persoon?*

(a) Police Officer (b) Ambulance Driver (c) Doctor

*681. Challenger Chris Kongo found the punches to stop defending WBO Global welterweight champion Luther Clay on 22 August 2020. In which round did the stoppage take place?*

(a) Seven (b) Eight (c) Nine

*682. Alexander Povetkin won the WBC interim world heavyweight title when he defeated the defending champion Dillian Whyte and with the victory he also gained the vacant WBC Diamond heavyweight crown in a contest that took place on 22 August 2020. The win by Povetkin came by a stoppage in which round?*

(a) Five (b) Six (c) Seven

*683. How many times was Alexander Povetkin floored for a count by Dillian Whyte in round four during the title contest?*

(a) Once (b) Twice (c) Three times

*684. Who was the referee of the Povetkin-Whyte title contest?*

(a) John Latham (b) Victor Loughlin (c) Mark Lyson

*685. Shawn Porter won the vacant WBC Silver welterweight title on 22 August 2020, defeating opponent Sebastian Formella by which method?*

(a) Three-round disqualification (b) Four-round knockout (c) Twelve-round points decision

*686. In which country did the Porter-Formella title contest take place?*

(a) America (b) Canada (c) Mexico

*687. Tim Tszyu retained his IBF Australasian super-welterweight title and his WBO Global Super-welterweight crown on 26 August 2020 when he stopped challenger Jeff Horn in which round?*

(a) Eight (b) Nine (c) Ten

**688. At which venue in Australia did the Tszyu-Horn title contest take place?**

(a) Rumours International, Toowoomba, Queensland (b) Bendigo Stadium, Bendigo, Victoria (c) Queensland Country Bank Stadium, Townsville, Queensland

**689. At this stage of his career Tim Tszyu was now undefeated in how many professional contests?**

(a) 16 (b) 17 (c) 18

**690. Daniel Dubois successfully defended his WBO International heavyweight title on 29 August 2020 when he stopped his challenger Ricardo Snijders in which round?**

(a) One (b) Two (c) Three

**691. Who was Daniel Dubois's trainer at the time of his contest with Ricardo Snijders?**

(a) Mark Tibbs (b) Martin Bowers (c) Dave Coldwell

**692. What is Daniel Dubois's nickname?**

(a) Dynamite (b) Bazooka (c) Short Fuse

**693. Sunny Edwards retained the IBF International super-flyweight championship in a contest that took place on 29 August 2020 by defeating his challenger Thomas Essomba by which method?**

(a) Four-round knockout (b) Six-round disqualification (c) 12-round points decision

**694. Jose Carlos Ramirez remained the WBC and WBO world super-lightweight title holder on the 29 August 2020 when he defeated his challenger Viktor Postol by a 12-round points decision. At this stage of his career Ramirez was now undefeated in how many professional contests?**

(a) 25 (b) 26 (c) 27

**695. Who was the referee of the Ramirez-Postol title contest?**

(a) Russell Mora (b) Mark Nelson (c) Marcos Rosales

**696. Akeem Ennis-Brown won the Commonwealth super-lightweight crown from defending champion Philip Bowes and also captured the vacant British super-lightweight title on 2 September 2020 by which method?**

(a) Six-round stoppage (b) Nine-round knockout (c) 12-round points decision

**697. Alex Dilmaghani failed to capture the European super-featherweight crown on 5 September 2020 when he was stopped in round 12 by defending champion Samir Ziani. How many successful defences of the title had Ziani now made?**

(a) One (b) Two (c) Three

*698. What was the nationality of Samir Ziani?*
(a) French (b) Italian (c) Spanish

*699. Jamel Herring retained the WBO world super-featherweight title on 5 September 2020 when he defeated his challenger Jonathan Oqueno by a disqualification in which round?*
(a) Six (b) Seven (c) Eight

*700. Two of the three judges present at ringside for the Herring-Oqueno title contest were Patricia-Morse Jarman and Julie Lederman. Who was the third official?*
(a) Tim Cheatham (b) Lisa Giampa (c) Gary Ritter

*701. On 12 September 2020 Anthony Yarde met opponent Dec Spelman in a ten-round contest and won when the referee stopped the bout in round six. Where in the UK was Yarde born?*
(a) London (b) Manchester (c) Liverpool

*702. Who was Anthony Yarde's trainer for the Spelman contest?*
(a) Xavier Miller (b) Tunde Ajayi (c) Mark Tibbs

*703. The IBF world cruiserweight title changed hands on 26 September 2020 when challenger Mairis Briedis defeated defending champion Yuniel Dorticos by which method?*
(a) Four-round stoppage (b) Eight-round disqualification (c) 12-round points decision.

*704. Dina Thorslund retained her WBO world female super-bantamweight crown when she outpointed her challenger Nina Radovanovic over ten rounds on 26 September 2020. In which country did this contest take place?*
(a)  Sweden (b) Denmark (c) Norway

*705. What is the recorded height of Dina Thorslund?*
(a) 5ft 4in (b) 5ft 5in (c) 5ft 6in

*706. On 26 September 2020 Charlie Edwards outpointed his opponent Kyle Williams over how many rounds?*
(a) Six (b) Eight (c) Ten

*707. Josh Taylor retained his WBA super version of the world super-lightweight crown and the IBF world super-lightweight title on 26 September 2020 when he knocked out his challenger Apinun Khongsong in the opening stanza. How many first-round victories had Taylor now achieved during his professional career?*
(a) Four (b) Five (c) Six

**708. Who was Josh Taylor's trainer at the time of the Apinun Khongsong world title defence?**

(a) Adam Booth (b) Ben Davison (c) Chris Sanigar

**709. Prior to his title world challenge to Josh Taylor, Apinun Khongsong had been undefeated in how many professional contests?**

(a) 15 (b) 16 (c) 17

**710. Jermall Charlo retained his WBC world middleweight crown on 26 September 2020 when he outpointed his challenger Sergiy Derevyanchenko over 12 rounds. Who was the referee of this title contest?**

(a) Harvey Dock (b) Johnny Callas (c) Laurence Cole

**711. In a unification world title contest which took place on 26 September 2020, Jermell Charlo defended his WBC super-welterweight crown against Jeison Rosario, who was putting the WBA super version of the crown along with the IBF version of the championship on the line. Charlo emerged victorious when he knocked out Rosario in which round?**

(a) Seven (b) Eight (c) Nine

**712. Luis Nery won the vacant WBC world super-bantamweight championship on 26 September 2020 when he outpointed his opponent Aaron Alameda over 12 rounds. At this stage of his career Nery was now undefeated in how many professional contests?**

(a) 29 (b) 30 (c) 31

**713. What is the nationality of Luis Nery?**

(a) Mexican (b) American (c) Cuban

**714. John Riel Casimero retained his WBO world bantamweight crown on 26 September 2020 when he stopped his challenger Duke Micah in which round?**

(a) Two (b) Three (c) Four

**715. Two of the three judges present at ringside for the Casimero-Micah world title contest were Tim Cheatham and Julie Lederman, but who was the third official?**

(a) John McKaie (b) Kevin Morgan (c) Tom Carusone

**716. Ohara Davies won the WBC International super-lightweight title on 30 September 2020 when he defeated holder Tyrone McKenna by which method?**

(a) Six-round stoppage (b) Eight-round retirement (c) Ten round points decision?

**717. Who was the referee of the Davies-McKenna title contest?**

(a) John Latham (b) Phil Edwards (c) Steve Gray

**718. Prior to meeting Ohara Davies, how many successful defences of the WBC international super-lightweight title had Tyrone McKenna made?**
(a) One (b) Two (c) Three

**719. Hironobu Matsunaga retained his Japanese super-welterweight title on 3 October 2020 when he stopped challenger Yuto Shimizu in which round?**
(a) Six (b) Seven (c) Eight

**720. Chantelle Cameron won the vacant WBC world female super-lightweight title on 4 October 2020 when she defeated opponent Adriana dos Santos Araujo by which method?**
(a) Five-round retirement (b) Eight-round disqualification (c) Ten-round points decision

**721. At this stage of her career Chantelle Cameron was now undefeated in how many professional contests?**
(a) 12 (b) 13 (c) 14

**722. What was the nationality of Adriana dos Santos Araujo?**
(a) Italian (b) Brazilian (c) Spanish

**723. Joshua Buatsi remained the WBA International light-heavyweight champion on 4 October 2020 when he stopped challenger Mark Calic in which round?**
(a) Six (b) Seven (c) Eight

**724. On 9 October 2020 Emanuel Navarrete boxed his way to a 12-round points decision over his opponent Ruben Villa to win the vacant WBO world featherweight title. In which country did this contest take place?**
(a) America (b) Mexico (c) Argentina

**725. Liam Williams retained the British middleweight crown on 10 October 2020 when he knocked out challenger Andrew Robinson in which round?**
(a) One (b) Two (c) Three

**726. What was Liam Williams's nickname?**
(a) The Steam Roller (b) The Crusher (c) The Machine

**727. Where in the UK was Liam Williams born?**
(a) Scotland (b) Wales (c) England

**728. On 10 October 2020 Nathan Gorman outpointed opponent Richard Lartey over how many rounds?**
(a) Six (b) Eight (c) Ten

**729. Joana Pastrana won the European female minimum weight title when, on 16 October 2020, she defeated opponent Catalina Diaz by which method for the vacant title?**
(a) Six-round stoppage (b) Eight-round disqualification (c) Ten round points decision.

**730. What is the nationality of Joana Pastrana?**
(a) Italian (b) Spanish (c) Swedish

**731. In a unification bout Teofimo Lopez retained his IBF world lightweight title in a contest which took place on 17 October 2020 and in so doing also won the WBA super version of the world lightweight and WBO world lightweight crowns from holder Vasiliy Lomachenko by which method?**
(a) Six-round stoppage (b) Eight-round knockout (c) 12-round points decision

**732. How many years of age was Teofimo Lopez at the time of his victory over Lomachenko?**
(a) 22 (b) 23 (c) 24

**733. At this stage of his career Teofimo Lopez was now undefeated in how many professional contests?**
(a) 15 (b) 16 (c) 17

**734. Lewis Ritson won the vacant WBA inter-continental super-lightweight crown on 17 October 2020 when he defeated opponent Miguel Vazquez by which method?**
(a) Six-round disqualification (b) Nine-round retirement (c) 12-round points decision

**735. Jay Harris boxed his way to a points decision over opponent Marcel Braithwaite on 18 October 2020. Over how many rounds was the contest scheduled?**
(a) Eight (b) Ten (c) Twelve

**736. Roman Gonzalez had a successful night on 23 October 2020 when he retained his WBA super world super-flyweight crown against challenger Israel Gonzalez by which method?**
(a) Five-round stoppage (b) Nine-round knockout (c) 12-round points decision

**737. Juan Francisco Estrado kept hold of his WBC world super-flyweight title on 23 October 2020 when he stopped his challenger Carlos Cuadras in round 11. Who was the referee of the title contest?**
(a) Jose Guadalupe Garcia (b) Abdiel Barragan (c) Jack Reiss

**738. On 31 October 2020 Amy Timlin and Carly Skelly stepped into the ring to contest the vacant Commonwealth female super-bantamweight title. What was the result?**
(a) Ten-round points win for Amy Timlin (b) Ten-round win points win for Carly Skelly (c) Ten-round draw

**739. Oleksandr Usyk won the WBO inter-continental heavyweight championship on 31 October 2020 when he outpointed defending title holder Dereck Chisora over 12 rounds. At this stage of his career Usyk was now undefeated in how many professional contests?**
(a) 18 (b) 19 (c) 20

**740. On 31 October 2020 Savannah Marshall stepped out of the ring after winning the vacant WBO world female middleweight title after stopping her opponent Hannah Rankin in which round?**
(a) Six (b) Seven (b) Eight (c) Nine

**741. Who was the referee of the Marshall-Rankin title contest?**
(a) Phil Edwards (b) Victor Loughlin (c) Robert Williams

**742. George Kambosos jr emerged victorious on 31 October 2020 when he crossed gloves with opponent Lee Selby, winning by way of a 12-round points decision. What is the nationality of Kambosos Jr?**
(a) Italian (b) Australian (c) American

**743. Tommy McCarthy captured the vacant European cruiserweight crown on 31 October 2020 when he defeated opponent Bilal Laggoune by which method?**
(a) Eight-round stoppage (b) Ten-round knockout (c) 12-round points decision

**744. Naoya Inoue retained his WBA super version of the world bantamweight crown and the IBF world bantamweight title on 31 October 2020 when he stopped challenger Jason Moloney in round seven. In which country did the contest take place?**
(a) America (b) Japan (c) Australia

**745. The WBC world female bantamweight title changed hands on 31 October 2020 when defending champion Mariana Juarez lost her crown to challenger Yulihan Alejandra Luna Avila by which method?**
(a) Six-round stoppage (b) Nine-round knockout (c) Ten-round points decision

**746. On 13 November 2020 Denzel Bentley became the new British middleweight champion when he won the vacant title by defeating opponent Mark Heffron who retired in which round?**
(a) Three (b) Four (c) Five

**747. Who was the referee of the Bentley-Heffron title contest?**
(a) Michael Alexander (b) John Latham (c) Steve Gray

**748. On 14 November 2020 Terri Harper retained her WBC and IBO female world super-feather titles when she stopped her challenger Katharina Thanderz in which round?**
(a) Seven (b) Eight (c) Nine

*749. At the time of the Harper-Thanderz title contest who was the reigning WBO female world super-featherweight champion?*

(a) Mikaela Mayer (b) Ewa Brodnicka (c) Ramona Kuehne

*750. Katie Taylor put her WBC, WBA, IBF and WBO female world lightweight titles on the line against challenger Miriam Gutierrez on 14 November 2020 and left the ring victorious, defeating her opponent by which method?*

(a) Six-round stoppage (b) Eight-round disqualification (c) Ten-round points decision

*751. During the title contest Miriam Gutierrez was floored for a count by Katie Taylor in which round?*

(a) Four (b) Six (c) Eight

*752. Rachel Ball became the new interim WBC world female super-bantamweight title holder after defeating opponent Jorgelina Guanini by which method in a contest which took place on 14 November 2020?*

(a) Eight-round disqualification (b) Nine-round retirement (c) Ten-round points decision

*753. Ukashir Farooq won the vacant WBA Continental bantamweight championship on 14 November 2020 when he defeated opponent Angel Aviles by which method?*

(a) Four-round stoppage (b) Six-round knockout (c) Ten-round points decision

*754. Terence Crawford retained his WBO world welterweight crown against challenger Kell Brook on 14 November 2020 by a stoppage in which round?*

(a) Three (b) Four (c) Five

*755. At this stage of his career, Terence Crawford was now undefeated in how many professional contests?*

(a) 35 (b) 36 (c) 37

*756. What is Terence Crawford's nickname?*

(a) Bud (b) The Technician (c) Mr Smooth

*757. On 21 November 2020 Conor Benn made a successful defence of his WBA Continental welterweight title by defeating his challenger Sebastian Formella by which method?*

(a) Three-round knockout (b) Six-round stoppage (c) Ten-round points decision.

*758. At this stage of his career Conor Benn was now undefeated in how many professional contests?*

(a) 16 (b) 17 (c) 18

*759. In which country did the Benn-Formella title contest take place?*

(a) England (b) Germany (c) France

*760. Chayaphon Moonsri became a former champion on 27 November 2020 when he lost his WBC world minimum title by way of a 12-round points decision to challenger Panya Pradabsri. Prior to this bout, Moonsri had been undefeated in how many professional contests.*

(a) 53 (b) 54 (c) 55

*761. On 28 November 2020 Joe Joyce captured the vacant European heavyweight crown and in so doing he also won the British and Commonwealth plus the WBC silver and WBO international heavyweight titles when he knocked out the defending champion Daniel Dubois in which round?*

(a) 10 (b) 11 (c) 12

*762. Billy Joe Saunders successfully defended his WBO world super-middleweight title on 4 December 2020 when he defeated his challenger Martin Murray by which method?*

(a) Three-round knockout (b) Five-round disqualification (c) 12-round points decision

*763. In a contest scheduled for eight rounds on 4 December 2020, Shannon Courtenay emerged victorious when she stopped her opponent Dorota Norek in which round?*

(a) Four (b) Six (c) Seven

*764. Lyndon Arthur retained his Commonwealth light-heavyweight crown and also won the vacant WBO Intercontinental light-heavyweight title on 5 December 2020 when he defeated Anthony Yarde by which method?*

(a) Three-round stoppage (b) Eight-round knockout (c) 12-round points decision.

*765. Errol Spence Jr boxed his way to a 12-round points decision over challenger Danny Garcia on 5 December 2020 to retain his WBC and IBF world welterweight titles. Who was the referee of the contest?*

(a) Thomas Taylor (b) Jon Schorle (c) Laurence Cole

*766. At this stage of his career Errol Spence Jr was now undefeated in how many professional contests?*

(a) 27 (b) 28 (c) 29

*767. Sam Eggington stopped his opponent Ashley Theophane in the sixth round on 11 December 2020. How many rounds was the contest scheduled for?*

(a) Eight (b) Ten (c) 12

*768. At the time of the contest, Ashley Theophane was a former British champion in which weight division?*
(a) Lightweight (b) Super-lightweight (c) Welterweight

*769. What is Sam Eggington's nickname?*
(a) The Savage (b) The Beast (c) The Bear

*770. Lourdes Juarez won the WBC world female super flyweight title on 12 December 2020 when she defeated defending champion Guadalupe Martinez Guzman by which method?*
(a) Three-round knockout (b) Five-round stoppage (c) Ten-round points decision

*771. On 12 December 2020 Anthony Joshua retained the WBA super version of the world heavyweight crown and also retained the IBF, WBO and IBO world heavyweight titles when he knocked out his challenger Kubrat Pulev in round nine. The referee of the title contest was Deon Dwarte. What was Dwarte's nationality?*
(a) German (b) Australian (c) South African

*772. Lawrence Okolie won the vacant WBO International cruiserweight crown on 12 December 2020 when he stopped his opponent Nikodem Jezewski in which round?*
(a) One (b) Two (c) Three

*773. Prior to Lawrence Okolie, who was the previous holder of the WBO International cruiserweight title?*
(a) Tony Bellew (b) Noel Gevor (c) Artur Mann

*774. In a contest that took place on 12 December 2020, Hughie Fury won his bout when he outpointed his opponent Mariusz Wach over how many rounds?*
(a) Eight (b) Ten (c) 12

*775. Shakur Stevenson outpointed his opponent Toka Kahn Clary over the duration of ten rounds on 12 December 2020. In which country did the contest take place?*
(a) Japan (b) Mexico (c) America

*776. On 17 December 2020, Gamal Yafai stepped into the ring to challenge for the European super-bantamweight crown and became the new title holder when he defeated defending champion Luca Rigoldi by which method?*
(a) Three-round knockout (b) Four-round retirement (c) 12-round points decision

*777. Who was the referee of the Yafai-Rigoldi title contest?*
(a) Robin Dolpierre (b) Fabian Guggenheim (c) Daniel Van de Wiele

*778. In which country did the Yafai-Rigoldi title contest take place?*
(a) Italy (b) England (c) Spain

*779. Craig Richards became the new British light-heavyweight champion on 18 December 2020 when he stopped the reigning title holder Shakan Pitters in which round?*

(a) Seven (b) Eight (c) Nine

*780. What is Craig Richards's nickname?*

(a) Spider (b) Wasp (c) Hornet

*781. Gennady Golovkin remained the IBF and IBO world middleweight champion on 18 December 2020 when his challenger Kamil Szeremeta retired in round seven. Who was the referee of this contest?*

(a) Chris Young (b) Frank Gentile (c) Telis Assimenios

*782. Hyun Mi Choi retained her WBA world female super-featherweight crown on 18 December 2020 when she defeated her challenger Calista Silgado by which method?*

(a) Six-round stoppage (b) Nine-round knockout (c) Ten-round points decision

*783. Gilberto Ramirez became the new North American Boxing Federation light-heavyweight champion on 18 December 2020 when he stopped defending title holder Alfonso Lopez in which round?*

(a) Eight (b) Nine (c) Ten

*784. At this stage of his career Gilberto Ramirez was now undefeated in how many professional contests?*

(a) 40 (b) 41 (c) 42

*785. Saul Alvarez captured the WBA super version of the world super-middleweight title on 19 December 2020 when he outpointed defending champion Callum Smith over 12 rounds and in so doing also won the vacant WBC world middleweight crown. At this stage of his career Alvarez had now participated in how many professional contests?*

(a) 57 (b) 58 (c) 59

*786. Ilunga Makabu made a first successful defence of the WBC world cruiserweight championship in a contest that took place on 19 December 2020 when he knocked out his challenger Olanrewaju Durodola in which round?*

(a) Six (b) Seven (c) Eight

*787. On 19 December 2020 Ibeth Zamora Silva retained her WBC world female flyweight title when she outpointed her challenger Gabriela Sanchez Saavedra over ten rounds. In which country did this contest take place?*

(a) Mexico (b) Argentina (c) America

**788. Christina Hammer shared the ring with her opponent Sanna Turunen on 20 December 2020 to contest the vacant WIBF super-middleweight world title and became the new champion when she won by a knockout in which round?**

(a) Six (b) Seven (c) Eight

**789 At this stage of her career Christina Hammer had now participated in how many professional contests?**

(a) 28 (b) 29 (c) 30

**790. How many bouts did Christina Hammer participate in during the course of 2020?**

(a) One (b) Two (c) Three

**791. On 31 December 2020 Kazuto Ioka retained his WBO world super-flyweight title when he stopped his challenger Kosei Tanaka in which round?**

(a) Six (b) Seven (c) Eight

**792. Who was the referee of the Ioka-Tanaka title contest?**

(a) Jose Hiram Rivera (b) Michiaki Someya (c) Celestino Ruiz

**793. Prior to his WBO world super-flyweight challenge to Kazuto Ioka, Kosei Tanaka was undefeated in how many professional contests?**

(a) 14 (b) 15 (c) 16

**794. Before his challenge for the WBO world super-flyweight crown Kosei Tanaka had held a world championship in how many different weight divisions?**

(a) One (b) Two (c) Three

**795. Ryan Garcia won the vacant interim WBC world lightweight title on 2 January 2021 when he knocked out Luke Campbell in which round?**

(a) Five (b) Six (c) Seven

**796. Before punching his way to victory, Ryan Garcia was floored for a count by Luke Campbell in which round?**

(a) One (b) Two (c) Three

**797. Who was the referee of the Garcia-Campbell title contest?**

(a) Laurence Cole (b) Jack Reiss (c) Tony Weeks

**798. At this stage of his career Ryan Garcia was now undefeated in how many professional contests?**

(a) 20 (b) 21 (c) 23

**799. What is Ryan Garcia's nickname?**

(a) King Ry (b) Princ Ry (c) Lord Ry

**800. Felix Alvarado retained his IBF world light-flyweight crown on 2 January 2021 when he stopped his challenger Deejay Kriel in which round?**

(a) Eight (b) Nine (c) Ten

# ANSWERS

## PROFESSIONAL DEBUTS

1. 1960
2. 1982
3. 1965
4. 1980
5. 1968
6. 1961
7. 1958
8. 1973
9. 1960
10. 1952
11. 1989
12. 1977
13. 1989
14. 1972
15. 1963
16. 1969
17. 1957
18. 1963
19. 1968
20. 1959

ROUND TWO
## FIRST PROFESSIONAL OPPONENTS

1. Albert Adams
2. Jim Thomas
3. Ray Gomez
4. Ted Fitzgerald
5. Glen Peck
6. Curtis Hightower
7. Colin McAuley
8. Rodell Dupree
9. Steve Flajole
10. Andrew DaCosta
11. John Borman
12. Domingo Rivera
13. Ray Coleman
14. Ramon Lugo
15. Santos Martins
16. Efren Chavez
17. Stephen Lee
18. Eddie Vallejo
19. Carmine Fotti
20. Billy Graydon

ROUND THREE
## LAST PROFESSIONAL OPPONENTS

1. Chester Slider
2. Rudy Marshall
3. Ernesto Herrera
4. Emmett Linton
5. Hiroyuki Murakami
6. Johnny Famechon
7. Darrell Flint
8. Joe Smith Jr
9. Leslie Stewart
10. Zolani Petelo
11. Duke Mckenzie
12. Tony Sibson
13. Rodrigo Valdez
14. John H. Stracey

15. Gerry Cooney
16. Willie Myles
17. Wayne Beale
18. Larry Boardman
19. Harry Walker
20. Carlos Bojorquez

ROUND FOUR
## OPPONENTS NOT MET IN A PROFESSIONAL CAREER

1. Thad Spencer
2. Jake LaMotta
3. Pinklon Thomas
4. Carl Froch
5. Kirkland Laing
6. Victor Galindez
7. Earnie Shavers
8. Tony Sibson
9. Alan Rudkin
10. Greg Page
11. Jun-Suk Hwang
12. Fred Hutchings
13. Tim Witherspoon
14. John McCluskey
15. Paul Hodkinson
16. Nino Valdes
17. Cuby Jackson
18. Efren Jimenez
19. Roger Rouse
20. Borge Krogh

ROUND FIVE
## WHAT YEAR WERE THEY BORN?

1. 1952
2. 1932
3. 1938
4. 1972
5. 1942
6. 1966
7. 1945
8. 1944
9. 1919
10. 1965
11. 1960
12. 1935
13. 1930
14. 1956
15. 1923
16. 1947
17. 1968
18. 1948
19. 1943
20. 1966

ROUND SIX
## NICKNAMES

1. Homicide Hank
2. Dark Destroyer
3. Desert Storm
4. Old Bones
5. The Orchid Man
6. Ragamuffin Man

7 .The Lion
8. The Brown Bomber
9. The Brockton Blockbuster
10. Old Mongoose
11. Pocket Rocket
12. The Clones Cyclone
13.The Professor
14. Will o' the Wisp
15. The Hawk
16. T-Rex
17. The Tartan Tornado
18. Iron Mike
19. Camden Buzzsaw
20. Man of Steel

ROUND SEVEN
## MORE NICKNAMES

1. Wilfredo Gomez
2. Christy Martin
3. James DeGale
4. Michael Dokes
5. Terry Marsh
6. Oscar De La Hoya
7. Vasiliy Lomachenko
8. Milton McCrory
9. James Toney
10. Danny Lopez
11. Callum Smith
12. Keith Thurman
13. Manny Pacquiao
14. Terry Downes
15. Chris Byrd
16. Dingaan Thobela
17. George Groves
18. Laila Ali
19. Pernell Whitaker
20. Arturo Gatti

ROUND EIGHT
## REAL NAMES

1. Cassius Marcellus Clay
2. Judah Bergman
3. Noah Brusso
4. Samuel Lazzara
5. Giuseppe Carrora
6. Carmine Tilelli
7. Thomas Rocco Barbella
8. Stanislaw Kiecal
9. Gershon Mendeloff
10. Giuseppe Antonio Berardinelli
11. Archibald Lee Wright
12. Maxwell Antonio Loach
13. Joseph Francis Anthony Hagen
14. Gugliermo Papaleo
15. Henry L. Pylkowski
16. Walker Smith Jr
17. Joseph Paul Zukauskas
18.  Richard Ihetu
19. Arnold Raymond Cream
20. Jonathon Gutenko

ROUND NINE
## MIDDLE NAMES

1. Adetokunboh
2. Lamont
3. Demont
4. William
5. Mack
6. Albert
7. Livingstone
8. Edward
9. Lloyd
10. William
11. Martin
12. Alphonse
13. Nathaniel
14. Juan
15. Christian
16. Edmund
17. John
18.  Fitzgerald
19. Anthony
20.  Leshun

ROUND TEN
## MORE MIDDLE NAMES

1. Jerome
2. Oblitey
3. Allan
4. Henry
5. Jackson
6. Charles
7. Claudius
8. Andres
9. Patrick
10. William
11. McKenzie
12. Lee
13. David
14. Hunter
15. Maria
16. Odell
17. Deon
18. Craig
19. Gerard
20. Dwayne

ROUND ELEVEN
## WHERE WERE THEY BORN?

1. Argentina
2. Denmark
3. Mexico
4. Panama
5. Japan
6. Italy
7. Brazil
8. Sweden
9. Canada
10. Spain
11. Cuba
12. Argentina
13 Germany
14. Philippines

15. America
16. Venezuela
17. America
18. South Africa
19. America
20. Russia

ROUND TWELVE
## FIRST DEFEAT

1. Joe Frazier
2. Omar Amaya
3. Alex Arthur
4. Harry Craster
5. Eddie Duncan
6. Hugo Inocencio Saavedra
7. Juan Aguilar
8. Floyd Mayweather Jr
9. Carl Thompson
10. Clinton Mitchell
11. John Michael Johnson
12. Ross Puritty
13. Marty Marshall
14. Juan Diaz
15. Peter Brown
16. Derrick Kelly
17. Jock Leslie
18. James Douglas
19. Victor Paul
20. Harold Petty

ROUND THIRTEEN
## HOW MANY PROFESSIONAL BOUTS

1. 55
2. 30
3. 69
4. 44
5. 46
6. 23
7. 65
8. 143
9. 25
10. 75
11. 126
12. 52
13. 41
14. 38
15. 64
16. 121 (This figure includes a bout declared a no contest)
17. 46
18. 32
19. 51
20. 43 (This figure includes a bout declared a no contest)

ROUND FOURTEEN
## FIRST ROUND VICTORIES

1. Two
2. 13
3. Eight
4. Five
5. Four

6. Seven
7. 15
8. 10
9. Seven
10. Three
11. Five
12. 11
13. Nine
14. Eight
15. Five
16. 20
17. Three
18. Eight
19. Eight
20. 14

ROUND FIFTEEN
## BRITISH CHAMPIONS

1. Light-heavyweight
2. Super-flyweight
3. Super-welterweight
4. Welterweight
5. Lightweight
6. Lightweight
7. Cruiserweight
8. Heavyweight
9. Super-featherweight
10. Featherweight
11. Middleweight
12. Super-bantamweight
13. Bantamweight
14. Bantamweight
15. Super-welterweight
16. Welterweight
17. Super-lightweight
18. Flyweight
19. Super-middleweight
20. Heavyweight

ROUND SIXTEEN
## COMMONWEALTH CHAMPIONS

1. Super-featherweight
2. Featherweight
3. Super-flyweight
4. Welterweight
5. Super-bantamweight
6. Super-bantamweight
7. Welterweight
8. Middleweight
9. Super-lightweight
10. Super-featherweight
11. Heavyweight
12. Light-heavyweight
13. Light-heavyweight
14. Middleweight
15. Cruiserweight
16. Middleweight
17. Bantamweight
18. Light-heavyweight
19. Super-welterweight
20. Super-welterweight

## EUROPEAN CHAMPIONS

1. Bantamweight
2. Super-welterweight
3. Bantamweight
4. Flyweight
5. Light-heavyweight
6. Heavyweight
7. Super-middleweight
8. Cruiserweight
9. Super-featherweight
10. Flyweight
11. Super-bantamweight
12. Light-heavyweight
13. Welterweight
14. Super-lightweight
15. Lightweight
16. Super-middleweight
17. Super- welterweight
18. Welterweight
19. Heavyweight
20. Middleweight

## WORLD CHAMPIONS

1. WBO super-featherweight
2. WBC Cruiserweight
3. WBA flyweight
4. Undisputed welterweight
5. WBC super-welterweight.
6. WBA Heavyweight
7. Undisputed bantamweight
8. WBA lightweight
9. Undisputed flyweight
10. WBO cruiserweight
11. WBA super-middleweight
12. WBA light-flyweight
13. WBA super- bantamweight
14. WBC super-flyweight
15. IBF super-lightweight
16. Undisputed light-heavyweight
17. Undisputed middleweight
18. WBA heavyweight
19. Undisputed flyweight
20. Undisputed welterweight

## IN WHICH WEIGHT DIVISION

1. Undisputed lightweight
2. WBA super-welterweight
3. Undisputed light-heavyweight
4. WBO light-heavyweight
5. WBA super-lightweight
6. WBO light-heavyweight
7. Undisputed featherweight
8. WBC lightweight
9. Undisputed light-heavyweight
10. WBC super-middleweight
11. Undisputed flyweight
12. WBA bantamweight
13. WBC middleweight
14. WBC lightweight
15. WBA flyweight
16. Undisputed light-heavyweight
17. WBA lightweight
18. WBC middleweight
19. WBC flyweight
20. WBO flyweight

## NAME THE REFEREE

1. Eddie Graney
2. Robert P. Watson
3. Jack Welsh
4. Dick Nugent
5. Johnny Gallagher
6. Tommy Sheridan
7. Eddie Forbes
8. Arthur Donovan
9. Moss Deyong
10. Willie Smith
11. Harry Kessler
12. Tommy Hart
13. Irineo Gallegos
14. Ramon Berumen
15. Jersey Joe Walcott
16. Johnny LoBianco
17. Lorenzo Fortunato
18. Richard Green
19. Larry Rozadilla
20. Isidro Rodriguez

## MORE NAME THE REFEREE

1. Davy Miller
2. Arthur Donovan
3. Ike Powell
4. Harry Gibbs
5. Larry Rozadilla
6. Tom Kelly
7. Octavio Meyran
8. Jackie Keough
9. Ray Solis
10. Joey Curtis
11. Roberto Ramirez Snr
12. Robert Palmer
13. Richard Steele
14. Ismael Wiso Fernandez
15. Eddie Cotton
16. Paul Thomas
17. Daniel Van de Wiele
18. Marcos Rosales
19. Howard Foster
20. Ian John Lewis

## WHICH COUNTRY

1. Spain
2. Canada
3. Sweden
4. Italy
5. Spain
6. America
7. Germany
8. Italy

9. England
10. Spain
11. Australia
12. Italy
13. America
14. England
15. Italy
16. Canada
17. South Africa
18. Japan
19. Spain
20. America

ROUND TWENTY-THREE
## HOW TALL

1. 6ft 3in
2. 6ft 2½in
3. 6ft 3in
4. 6ft 5in
5. 6ft 2in
6. 5ft 7in
7. 6ft
8. 6ft 3in
9. 6ft 3in
10. 5ft 11½in
11. 6ft 2in
12. 6ft 1in
13. 6ft 1in
14. 6ft 3in
15. 6ft
16. 6ft 1in
17. 6ft 3in
18. 6ft 3in
19. 5ft 10in
20. 6ft 3½in

ROUND TWENTY-FOUR
## Medal Winners at the Olympic Games

1. American
2. Albert Oldman
3. Flyweight
4. Gold
5. Three: The said winners being Vittorio Tamagnini (Bantamweight) Carlo Orlandi (Lightweight) Piero Toscani (Middleweight)
6. Flyweight
7. Gold
8. Middleweight
9. Floyd Patterson
10. Flyweight
11. Gold
12. Joe Frazier
13. Middleweight
14. Cuban
15. Nine: Said winners being Paul Gonzales (Light-flyweight) Steve McCrory (Flyweight) Meldrick Taylor (Featherweight) Pernell Whitaker (Lightweight) Jerry Page (Light-welterweight) Mark Breland (Welterweight) Frank Tate (Light-middleweight) Henry Tillman (Heavyweight) Tyrell Biggs (Super-heavyweight)
16. Gold
17. Heavyweight

18. Mario Kindelan
19. Lightweight
20. French

ROUND TWENTY-FIVE
## FILMS

1. Ward Bond
2. Freddie Mills
3. Wrestler
4. Tommy Farr
5. Jersey Joe Walcott
6. Rocky Graziano
7. Billy Walker
8. John Gully MP
9. Archie Moore
10. Ken Norton
11. Joe Frazier
12. Jake LaMotta
13. Tommy Morrison
14. Rubin Carter
15. Michael Bentt
16. Lucia Rijker
17. James J. Braddock
18. Mike Tyson
19. Mark Wahlberg
20. Tony Bellew

ROUND TWENTY-SIX
## MORE FILMS

1. Abe Simon
2. Max Baer
3. Ingemar Johansson
4. Super-lightweight
5. Archie Moore
6. Sonny Liston
7. Rocky Graziano
8. Sugar Ray Robinson
9. Billy Walker
10. Jack O'Halloran
11. Ken Norton
12. Jack O'Halloran
13. Vito Antuofermo
14. Randall 'Tex' Cobb
15. Lennox Lewis v Wladimir Klitschko
16. Gary Stretch
17. Antonio Tarver
18. George Foreman
19. Howard Winstone
20. Roberto Duran

ROUND TWENTY-SEVEN
## FIND THE SOUTHPAW

1. Cornelius Boza-Edwards
2. Joe Calzaghe
3. Chad Dawson
4. James DeGale
5. Andre Dirrell
6. Tiger Flowers
7. Krzysztof Glowacki
8. Marvin Hagler
9. Maurice Hope
10. Zab Judah
11. Rafael Limon

12. Sergio Martinez
13. Alan Minter
14. Michael Moorer
15. Manny Pacquiao
16. Jackie Paterson
17. Vicente Saldivar
18. Corrie Sanders
19. Billy Joe Saunders
20. Adonis Stevenson

ROUND TWENTY-EIGHT
## WOMEN IN BOXING

1. Carol Polis
2. Eva Shain
3. Jane Couch
4. Eugenia Williams
5. Tania Follett
6. Ten round points decision
7. Kaye
8. 2007
9. Laila Ali
10. Judith Rollestone
11. Middleweight
12. Natasha Jonas
13. First Lady
14. Five Round retirement
15. 1981
16. Irish
17. 5ft 8in
18. Master of Ceremonies
19. Shannon Courtenay
20. Debbie Down

ROUND TWENTY-NINE
## BOXING BROTHERS

1. Rahman
2. Buddy
3. Gaby
4. Bruce
5. Andre
6. Glenn
7. Don
8. Robert
9. Joe
10. Matthew
11. Haroon
12. Joey
13. Ernie
14. Steve
15. Orlin
16. Ray
17. Leon
18. Nate
19. Rogelio
20. Marsellos

ROUND THIRTY
## WORLD CHAMPIONSHIP CONTESTS

1. Australia
2. America
3. France
4. England
5. Cuba

6. America
7. Japan
8. Italy
9. Thailand
10. Germany
11. Ghana
12. Mexico
13. South Africa
14. Argentina
15. South Korea
16. Thailand
17. Spain
18. England
19. Italy
20. Germany

ROUND THIRTY-ONE
## MORE WORLD CHAMPIONSHIP CONTESTS

1. France
2. Cuba
3. Philippines
4. Canada
5. England
6. Canada
7. Venezuela
8. Denmark
9. Thailand
10. Italy
11. America
12. England
13. America
14. Brazil
15. South Africa
16. Denmark
17. Japan
18. Germany
19. Finland
20. Germany

ROUND THIRTY-TWO
## PROMOTERS AND MANAGERS

1 Bob
2. Mike
3. Lou
4. Mickey
5. Barney
6. Aileen
7. Tania
8. Barry
9. Eddie
10. Mick
11. Jackie
12. Don
13. Terry
14. Harry
15. Kellie
16. Mogens
17. Tex
18. Jack
19. Frank
20. Jim

ROUND THIRTY-THREE
## MORE PROMOTERS AND MANAGERS

1. Jarvis
2. Bruce
3. George
4. Julian
5. Arthur
6. Ted
7. Miranda
8. Gus
9. Tommy
10. Alex
11. Mickey
12. Dennis
13. Harry
14. Mike
15. Jack
16. Cedric
17. George
18. Katherine
19. John
20. Chris

ROUND THIRTY-FOUR
## PHOTOGRAPH QUIZ

1. Tommy Farr
2. Rocky Marciano
3. Floyd Patterson
4. Johnny Pritchett
5. John McCluskey
6. Howard Winstone
7. Mark Rowe
8. Emile Griffith
9. Herbie Hide
10. Dennis Andries
11. Mike Tyson
12. Colin McMillan
13. Wayne McCullough
14. Naseem Hamed
15. Robin Reid
16. Tim Austin
17. Carl Thompson
18. Paul Ingle
19. Glenn Catley
20. Ricky Hatton

ROUND THIRTY-FIVE
## MORE PHOTOGRAPHS

1. Terry Lawless
2. Brian Curvis
3. Ken Buchanan
4. John Conteh
5. John H. Stracey
6. Alan Minter
7. Barry McGuigan
8. Lloyd Honeyghan
9. Terry Marsh
10. Herol Graham
11. Lennox Lewis
12. Carl Froch
13. Amir Khan
14. David Haye
15. Nathan Cleverly
16. Darren Barker
17. Kell Brook
18. Carl Frampton
19. Lee Selby
20. Callum Smith

ROUND THIRTY-SIX
## GENERAL QUIZ ANSWERS

1. 14
2. George Siler
3. 20
4. Stanley Ketchel
5. Six-round points decision
6. Wales
7. Polo Grounds, New York
8. Jack O'Sullivan
9. America
10. America
11. 78
12. Eddie Forbes
13. Ten
14. America
15. Six
16. Arthur Donovan
17. Ten
18. Red Robinson
19. 14
20. Eight-round retirement
21. Featherweight
22. 15-round points decision
23. Dave Crowley
24. Freddie Mills
25. Len Harvey
26. Ten
27. Paul Cavalier
28. Six
29. Ruby Goldstein
30. 54
31. Frankie Klick
32. Featherweight
33. 15-round points decision
34. Austrian
35. 15-round points decision
36. Teddy Waltham
37. Thailand
38. Jimmy Carruthers
39. Nine
40. Two
41. Harry Kessler
42. Yankee Stadium, Bronx, New York
43. Six
44. 49
45. A draw
46. Germany
47. Heavyweight
48. 21
49. 54
50. One
51. Featherweight
52. Seven-round retirement
53. Jack Hart
54. Cuban

55. 15-round points decision
56. Thailand
57. 57
58. Lorenzo Torreoalba
59. Davey Moore
60. 28
61. 31
62. One
63. Six
64. Ronnie James
65. 14
66. Jack Hart
67. Empire Pool, Wembley, London
68. Welterweight
69. Finland
70. Lightweight
71. One
72. Henry Cooper
73. Ten
74. Bantamweight
75. Sugar Ray Robinson
76. A draw
77. Italy
78. Argentine
79. 15-round points decision
80. 15-round points decision
81. Billy Jones
82. 26
83. Eight
84. 41
85. European
86. Wales
87. Super-lightweight
88. Seven
89. Johnny LoBianco
90. 29
91. 85
92. Three
93. Lightweight
94. Four
95. Jay Edson
96. German
97. Ten
98. Harry Gibbs
99. Royal Albert Hall, Kensington, London
100. Light-middleweight
101. Japan
102. Nine
103. Wally Thom
104. 13
105. Carlos Ortiz
106. Six
107. Roland Dakin
108. Empire Pool, Wembley, London
109. Five
110. Wally Thom
111. Howard Winstone
112. 15-round points decision
113. Zurich
114. Flyweight
115. Five
116. 28
117. 58

118. European
119. Joe Frazier
120. Points win for Griffith
121. Harry Gibbs
122. Denmark
123. Middleweight
124. 15
125. 15-round points decision
126. Harry Gibbs
127. 55
128. 35
129. 36
130. 21
131. Twice
132. Three
133. Three
134. 2000
135. Eight
136. Super-lightweight
137. Venezuelan
138. Five
139. Australia
140. Points win for Quarry
141. England
142. 15-round points decision
143. Quarry won by a one-round stoppage
144. Arthur Mercante
145. 15-round points decision
146. Four
147. Ken Brady
148. Iceland Arena, Melbourne, Victoria
149. Ten-round points decision
150. 43
151. Commonwealth
152. France
153. Five
154. 15
155. Nine
156. Tony Perez
157. Richfield Coliseum, Richfield, Ohio
158. Bayonne Bleeder
159. 43
160. 48
161. 13
162. Spain
163. Super-lightweight
164. 15-round points decision
165. Betulio Gonzalez
166. 12
167. Arthur Mercante
168. 41
169. 15-round points decision
170. England
171. Four
172. John L. Gardner
173. Six
174. Patrizio Oliva
175. Six
176. 18
177. Tim Witherspoon
178. 12-round points decision
179. 22
180. Six

181. Five
182. London Arena, Millwall, London
183. 17
184. 20
185. WBC Super-flyweight
186. Six
187. Points win for Cranmer
188. 66
189. Billy Walker
190. Seven
191. Mickey Vann
192. National Stadium, Cardiff, Wales
193. 24
194. 11
195. WBC
196. Four
197. 21
198. Joe Cortez
199. Caesars Palace, Las Vegas, Nevada
200. Three
201. Raul Caiz Sr
202. Riddick Bowe
203. 6ft 7in
204. British
205. Nine
206. Nine
207. Japan
208. Mark Johnson
209. 12-round points decision
210. Japan
211. Seven
212. America
213. Fleetwood Assassin
214. Five
215. Joe Cortez
216. Eight
217. Malcolm Bulner
218. Thailand
219. Hugo Rafael Soto
220. 11
221. America
222. Yorkshire Hunter
223. Four
224. Jamaica
225. Eight
226. Staples Center, Los Angeles, California
227. 14
228. 12-round point's decision
229. 7ft
230. Germany
231. Russian
232. Six
233. John Wright
234. Indonesia
235. 42
236. One
237. South Africa
238. 24
239. Seven
240. Kevin McIntyre
241. Mickey Vann
242. 17
243. Nonito Donaire

244. Eight
245. Canada
246. 13
247. 12-round points decision
248. Welterweight
249. Four
250. Denmark
251. Italian
252. WBC
253. Five
254. The Problem
255. WBO super-featherweight
256. WBA super-lightweight
257. Seven
258. Two
259. 31
260. Australia
261. 16
262. CJ Ross
263. Five
264. Audley Harrison
265. 12-round points decision
266. Five
267. Ukraine
268. Heavyweight
269. Six
270. Japan
271. Michael Griffin
272. Six
273. 12-round points decision
274. Three
275. 25
276. One
277. China
278. Cuban
279. Eight
280. 19
281. 22
282. Maksym Bursak
283. Italian
284. Ten-round points decision
285. Sparkle Lee
286. 27
287. Six
288. 24
289. 14
290. America
291. Carl Froch
292. IBF
293. Spanish
294. Eight
295. 18
296. Canada
297. One
298. 14
299. Lucas Browne
300. Super-heavyweight
301. Five
302. 37
303. 35
304. Columbian
305. Manchester Arena, Manchester, Lancashire
306. 12-round points decision

307. Tony Weeks
308. Esprit Arena Dusseldorf, Nordrhein-Westfalen
309. 68
310. 25
311. Five
312. Joerg Milke
313. 28
314. Germany
315. One
316. Robert Williams
317. 29
318. 12-round points decision
319. Two
320. Jean-Pierre Van Imschoot
321. Prince Charles
322. 12-round points decision
323. Second
324. Six
325. America
326. 49
327. 35
328. 12-round points decision
329. Five
330. Kevin Satchell
331. Eight
332. Terry O'Connor
333. WBO featherweight
334. 12-round points decision
335. Steve Willis
336. Eric Marlinski
337. 29
338. 12-round points decision
339. Three
340. One
341. Benjy Esteves Jr
342. 31
343. 12-round points decision
344. Harvey Dock
345. Barclays Center, Brooklyn, New York
346. WBO flyweight
347. WBA super world super-bantamweight and
     IBF super-bantamweight
348. The Jackal
349. Two
350. The Eagle
351. USC Soviet Wings, Moscow
352. Ten
353. The SSE Hydro, Glasgow, Scotland
354. Cuban
355. WBA super version and WBC Super-
     middleweight
356. 12-round points decision
357. Five
358. Three
359. 25
360. Seven
361. Ricky Gonzalez
362. Tank
363. Three
364. MGM Grand, Las Vegas, Nevada
365. 36
366. 12-round points decision
367. Ten

368. Featherweight
369. Five
370. Five
371. 11
372. David Fields
373. Five
374. Six
375. Twice
376. 68
377. 18
378. 28
379. Three
380. 41
381. 27
382. Six
383. Two
384. Eight
385. Bell Centre, Montreal, Quebec
386. Superman
387. Five
388. Four
389. A draw
390. 12-round points decision
391. England
392. 24
393. Two
394. Three
395. Germany
396. 16
397. Turkish
398. Seven
399. 13
400. 12
401. 12
402. America
403. Russian
404. German
405. Nine
406. IBF
407. Mexican
408. Six
409. 'IlCapo'
410. 12-round points decision
411. Canada
412. IBF
413. Ten
414. Seven
415. 40
416. The Bronze Bomber
417. 12-round points decision
418. 12-round point's decision
419. Principality Stadium, Cardiff, Wales
420. 24
421. Seven
422. Elland Road Football Ground, Leeds, Yorkshire
423. 26
424. America
425. Three
426. 24
427. Nine
428. 33
429. Ten-round points decision
430. Zimbabwe

431. Seven
432. Steve Gray
433. Super-heavyweight
434. 12
435. 12
436. Jason Moloney
437. Five
438. Scotland
439. 26
440. Ten-round points decision
441. Bulgaria
442. Eight
443. Terry O' Connor
444. Manchester Arena, Manchester, Lancashire
445. WBC
446. Bomber
447. A draw
448. Twice (round 9 and 12)
449. 6ft 7in
450. 6ft 9in
451. Jack Reiss
452. Staples Center, Los Angeles, California
453. Agit Kabayel
454. Super-featherweight
455. 12-round points decision
456. 31
457. WBC
458. Juggernaut
459. Super-heavyweight
460. Six
461. Greece
462. Ten-round points decision
463. Sparkle Lee
464. Gold
465. 12-round points decision
466. Bill Clancy
467. 12-round points decision
468. The SSE Hydro, Glasgow, Scotland
469. 14
470. 19
471. Gilberto Ramirez
472. Seven
473. Once (in round three)
474. Four (twice in round three and twice in round seven)
475. Michael Griffin
476. Destroyer
477. Julie Lederman
478. Madison Square Garden, New York
479. Ten-round points decision
480. Sparkle Lee
481. Three
482. 26
483. Vale Park Arena, Cardiff, Wales
484. 12 -round points decision
485. James Tennyson
486. Five
487. 11
488. 16
489. 21
490. 23
491. Hughie Fury
492. Eight

493. 22
494. 11
495. Nine
496. Polish
497. Seven
498. Japan
499. Two
500. 14
501. 11
502. 18
503. Krusher
504. Luis Pabon
505. Russia
506. 11
507. Bantamweight
508. Ten-round points decision
509. One
510. 19
511. A draw
512. Gold
513. 26
514. Points win for Golovkin
515. Two
516. 30
517. Robert Williams
518. 10
519. Silent Assassin
520. 13
521. Bantamweight
522. 12-round points decision
523. Shane McGuigan
524. Seven
525. 14
526. Seven (Sammy Reeson, Johnny Nelson (twice) Terry Dunstan, Carl Thompson (twice) David Haye, Enzo Maccarinelli, Tony Bellew)
527. Julie Lederman
528. Eight
529. 12
530. 15
531. Gold
532. 12-round points decision
533. Ernie Sharif
534. 11
535. 19
536. 46
537. Filipino Flash
538. Monster
539. Japan
540. Two
541. French
542. Japanese
543. Eleven
544. Staples Center, Los Angeles, California
545. Ray Corona
546. Patricia Morse Jarman
547. Argentine
548. 12
549. 29
550. Two
551. Two
552. Margaret Court Arena, Melbourne, Victoria
553. 12-round points decision

554. Georges Ory
555. Mexico
556. Mexican
557. Kenyan
558. Ten
559. 25
560. Super-lightweight
561. United Arab Emirates
562. 24
563. 12-round points decision
564. Five
565. Mark Lyson
566. Seven
567. MGM Grand, Grand Garden Arena, Las Vegas, Nevada
568. Ten
569. Ten-round point's decision
570. Diana Milani
571. Ten-round points decision
572. 21
573. 16
574. 6ft 6in
575. Gloria Martinez-Rizzo
576. Chinese
577. Three
578. Ten
579. 29
580. Seven
581. 12-round points decision
582. Luis Pabon
583. Nine
584. Saudi Arabia
585. The Body Snatcher
586. Two
587. Steve Weisfeld
588. Nine
589. Ten-round points decision
590. 11
591. Dillian Whyte
592. 12-round points decision
593. Charlie Edwards
594. Ten-round points decision
595. Seven
596. Twice (rounds three and five)
597. Kenny Bayless
598. MGM Grand, Grand Garden Arena, Las Vegas, Nevada
599. Nine
600. America
601. 12-round points decision
602. Laurence Cole
603. Once
604. Six
605. Ten
606. Tony Weeks
607. Seven
608. America
609. Points win for Takam
610. 12-round points decision
611. The Blade
612. Marcus McDonnell
613. Ten
614. Julie Lederman
615. David Price
616. Germany
617. 20
618. 2011
619. Ten
620. Tony Weeks
621. 28
622. Three
623. One
624. Michiaki Someya
625. Aioi Hall, Kariya, Aichi
626. 12-round points decision
627. 17
628. King Arthur
629. 12-round points decision
630. Welterweight
631. Six
632. Super-featherweight
633. Daniel Dubois
634. Nine
635. Commonwealth
636. 12-round points decision
637. Harvey Dock
638. 20
639. Dina Thorslund
640. Ten-round draw
641. 11
642. 11
643. Stefy Bull
644. Joe Gallagher
645. Victor Loughlin
646. Bronze
647. Two
648. Gold
649. Ten
650. Spain
651. Welterweight
652. Super-lightweight
653. Five
654. Master of ceremonies
655. American
656. Luke
657. Six
658. Eight
659. Devis Boschiero
660. Five
661. Middleweight
662. Eight
663. One
664. Five
665. Seven
666. Six
667. Ten
668. 14
669. Ten-round points decision
670. 36
671. 27
672. Karen Holderfield
673. America
674. Shannon Courtenay
675. 12-round points decision
676. 14
677. Three

678. Ten-round points decision
679. Ten (nine at lightweight and one in the super-lightweight division)
680. Police Officer
681. Nine
682. Five
683. Twice
684. Mark Lyson
685. 12-round points decision
686. America
687. Eight
688. Queensland County Bank Stadium, Townsville, Queensland
689. 16
690. Two
691. Martin Bowers
692. Dynamite
693. 12-round points decision
694. 26
695. Russell Mora
696. 12-round points decision
697. Two
698. French
699. Eight
700. Tim Cheatham
701. London
702. Tunde Ajayi
703. 12-round points decision
704. Denmark
705. 5ft 4in
706. Ten
707. Four
708. Ben Davison
709. 16
710. Harvey Dock
711. Eight
712. 31
713. Mexican
714. Three
715. John McKaie
716. Ten-round points decision
717. John Latham
718. Two
719. Seven
720. Ten-round points decision
721. 13
722. Brazilian
723. Seven
724. America
725. One
726. The Machine
727. Wales
728. Ten
729. Ten-round points decision
730. Spanish
731. 12-round points decision
732. 23
733. 16
734. 12-round points decision
735. Ten
736. 12-round points decision
737. Jose Guadalupe Garcia
738. Ten-round draw
739. 18
740. Seven
741. Phil Edwards
742. Australian
743. 12-round points decision
744. America
745. Ten-round points decision
746. Four
747. Steve Gray
748. Nine
749. Mikaela Mayer
750. Ten-round points decision
751. Four
752. Ten-round points decision
753. Ten-round points decision
754. Four
755. 37
756. Bud
757. Ten-round points decision
758. 17
759. England
760. 54
761. 10
762. 12-round points decision
763. Seven
764. 12-round points decision
765. Thomas Taylor
766. 27
767. Ten
768. Super-lightweight
769. The Savage
770. Ten-round points decision
771. South African
772. Two
773. Artur Mann
774. Ten
775. America
776. 12-round points decision
777. Fabian Guggenheim
778. Italy
779. Nine
780. Spider
781. Telis Assimenios
782. Ten-round points decision
783. Ten
784. 41
785. 57
786. Seven
787. Mexico
788. Seven
789. 28 (this includes one bout being declared a no contest)
790. Two
791. Eight
792. Michiaki Someya
793. 15
794. Three (WBO Minimum weight, WBO light-flyweight, WBO flyweight)
795. Seven
796. Two
797. Laurence Cole
798. 21
799. King Ry
800. Ten

Printed in Great Britain
by Amazon

35236244R00108